PLAY ON WORDS PUBLISHING ™

FOOLHARDY FOLK TALES

www.beansontoastmusic.com

For us

FOREWORD

I love a good folk tale. It's one of the main things that caught my attention, one rainy night back in around 2003, when I stumbled into my first lock-in at the legendary pub Nambucca on Holloway Road. I'd somehow found myself edging into a new circle of friends, they had a pub and a clubnight, and they seemed like a lot of fun. That night (it may or may not have been raining), a small acoustic guitar made an appearance once the doors had been bolted, and one of the guys who'd been working the bar began to sing some songs. They were basic, funny, moving, utterly unique, and they told the stories of the people around us. It was somehow very pure, the heart of what folk music is supposed to be, but also immediate, modern even.

The singer was Beans on Toast, of course, and a friendship began around that time that endures to this day. Beans helped persuade me to try playing an acoustic guitar and telling stories about my friends – I owe him an enormous musical debt – and together we've toured the world, got drunk, got into trouble, and spun tales about it all afterwards.

Reading Beans' first book, *Drunk Folk Stories*, was much like hearing his songs for the first time. Simple, direct, affecting, stories that stuck in my mind and made me creatively jealous. I'm pleased to say it wasn't a fluke, and that this second volume tops its predecessor. These pages immediately had me lost in nostalgia, laughter, melancholy and joy. Some of these stories I've been half-told over a beer sometime before; some of them are new to me. All of them reminded me why Beans is one of my favourite people in the world, a voice I'll always pay attention to, and you should too. He's a proper folksinger, a yarn-spinner, a character, a sage, and while he's undoubtedly hardy, he's no fool.

So, dear reader, pour yourself a drink, put your feet up, and dive in.

Frank Turner, Essex, 2021.

THE GREAT TESCO ROBBERY

"Fuck it." Dave leant in and grabbed the spliff that I'd been hoarding from between my fingers. He took a long, slow, thoughtful drag, held it for a second, then slowly and precisely blew the smoke out of the car window. Deep in thought, I could almost see the cogs turning as he looked me dead in the eye and said: "What have we got to lose?"

Looking back now, this was the beginning. This was when it became a reality. What had started as a joke had evolved into a conversation point, morphed into an obsession and now, after months of careful planning and scrutinising, now it was really happening. We were going to rob Tesco. And get away with it.

We were sitting in Dave's sky blue Ford Fiesta, or 'Sunshine' as she'd been affectionately named, parked up, down by the Wreck. I have no idea why the Wreck was called the Wreck, but it always had been. A barely used farmers road on the edge of the village, complete with a small river, a concrete bridge and a certain degree of privacy. As a kid I used to come here with my brother, skipping stones and the like, but ever since Dave got Sunshine we'd been using it as a smoking spot. We'd come down here most nights to get stoned on cheap hash and put the world to rights. It was here that we'd done most of our planning, it was here the whole thing had been concocted. Dave worked at one of Braintree's three Tescos, set slap bang in the middle of the horrific new build housing estate that had been carpet-bombed on the edge of Braintree town, 'Great Notley Garden Village' - even the name wound me up. Dave needed gainful employment to get a loan to get Sunshine, and we needed the car to get the fuck out of Braintree, or that was the plan. That was always the plan.

Dave initially worked weekends and the odd day while he did his A-Levels at Braintree college, but now college was done and dusted and there wasn't a massive amount of work going, he'd moved to full time. Of course, he could always join me at CSS Employment, a temping agency for the network of factories in and around the town. I had also just gone full time. Each week, I'd get sent out to a new factory and put to mind-numbing repetitive, unskilled work for nine hour shifts. I'd worked in bubble wrap factories, I'd built office dividers, put lids on bottles of vodka, put together plugs or car parts - the list goes on. One of the only benefits of the job was that you could get fired from one shit factory knowing full well CSS would find you work in another shit factory the following day. With this in mind, I'd pulled the rug out from a lot of jobsworth factory managers and been fired in all manner of ludicrous ways. Apart from that it was dire. But that didn't matter because it was only temporary. I'd signed up for the work part-time while I was doing my B-Tech in performing arts at the same college; now college was done, and I was working full time and still looking for my way to get the fuck out of Braintree.

That plan was, of course, Jellicoe: our band. We'd started playing two and a half years before, at school, and since then we'd lived and breathed for the band. We were good. Good enough to get played on the radio by John Peel. Good enough to draw a decent crowd to The Army & Navy in Chelmsford, and good enough for us to pin our hopes and dreams of an exciting life full of sex drugs and rock'n'roll on our music. But were we good enough to get there? That was the question we'd been forced to ask of late. A recent trip to London had proved pretty bleak: we'd hand-delivered our demo to every record label office in London, but nobody had been in touch. Nobody showed up to our recent gig at The Water Rats either, not just no one from the record labels or music industry - no one had shown up at all, and we'd played our hearts out to an empty room. Since then, we'd struggled to get other gigs in the city, and now that college had dispersed, the crowds at our Essex shows had started to dwindle, as people were beginning to work full time or move on with their lives.

The band consisted of me, Dave, and our best friend Jot. Jot didn't really like smoking weed, hence he didn't join us down the Wreck. He also didn't really like working, and since college, he'd just retreated to his mum and dad's house, to a world of lie-ins and daytime TV, much to the annoyance of both his parents. Jot didn't want to work in a shit factory or stacking shelves - why would he? The problem was that our band rehearsed in the 'Jam Room' a soundproofed shipping container at the bottom of Jot's garden. We'd bought it the year before, and being as Jot was the only one with a garden big enough to house it, Jot's Dad reluctantly agreed to let us keep it at theirs. It was brought in on the back of an articulated lorry, and now that it was there, it wasn't going anywhere. As far as I'm aware it still sits there to this day.

Since Jot had become a full time layabout, his dad had decided to lock the Jam Room, his hope being that Dave and I would join forces with him and make Jot get a job. It didn't work, and the Jam Room stayed locked - meaning we now had nowhere to rehearse, no gigs and no interest from the music industry or Joe Public. It started to look like we might need another way to get the fuck out of Braintree.

So we spent our evenings at the Wreck. Dave would clock off from work, swing home to grab some dinner, then drive around, pick me up and I'd skin up in the glove compartment en route. "Get this, right." Dave was bringing me up to speed with the goings-on of Great Notley Tescos, this was around six months prior to the aforementioned spliff. "A new lady started at work today: Shelia." As much as Dave hated his job, he had a huge fondness for the people he worked with and, as with any job, the drama was quite riveting to all involved. Of course, everyone loved Dave. As has always been the way, everybody I know loves Dave. Myself included. Even with his disdain for the company, the powers that be loved him, he was hard-working, reliable, easy on the eye and an absolute charmer to both his colleagues and the customers alike. They didn't do employee of the month, but if they did his pretty face would have been on that notice board as a permanent fixture. "And Sheila is no more than five foot tall, well over 50 years old, nice as pie but effectively a feeble old lady. And get this: she's the new head of security." I'll be honest; I was only half-listening, not as wrapped up in the Tesco staff soap opera as Dave was. I'd quite easily let his work chat roll over me, especially when I was stoned, which of course I was. I just raised my eyebrows in response. "Can you imagine how much fucking cash that place must make every day? The security is almost non-existent, but the last person doing that job, a guy called Mikey, looked like he could handle himself, if you know what I mean? Not that he did anything but sit and read the newspaper day in day out, but... Shelia. How the fuck would she act if you stuck a 9mm in her mouth and told her to give you the keys to the money room? She looks like my Nan." Dave was joking, of course; he wouldn't hurt a fly, didn't like guns, or violence or any of that nonsense. He was a big Wu-Tang Clan fan, but you know, that was different. I didn't reply. I left Dave's blasé comments about robbery floating in the air. Stupidly unrealistic, of course, but as far as hypothetical conversations go between the two of us when stoned, pretty mild. I pushed the *36 Chambers* cassette into the player, and the conversation moved on.

The next day when Dave picked me up, he'd been doing the maths. "Eight hours on the till today, I personally took around ten grand. So that's around £1,250 an hour. There are 20 tills open for 12 hours each day. That means they must be taking over £250,000 every day, and that's a Tuesday - Saturdays are twice as busy. They must be clearing nearly half a mil on a Saturday." I agreed it was a tremendous amount of money. What would the world look like if we had that kind of cash? We spent the whole night fantasising about life with half a million quid. It's not that Dave or I were flat broke - far from it. We were both raised by loving families in gainful employment and both had steady jobs, food on the table, roofs over our heads and the luxury that comes with suburban living. I wouldn't even say we were cash hungry, or particularly inspired by money. What we dreamed of was adventure, some kind of excitement that this town was not going to provide. Maybe New York; with that kind of cash it would be easy to start over in the midst of a big city like that; or maybe Thailand, raving under a full moon on a beach, wading in the clear blue sea, with cash like that we could open up a beach bar, spend our days in paradise; or backpacking around India, or bungee jumping in New Zealand... We could probably afford to do all the above, a life of travels on the road around the globe, it sounded epic. It's what I thought about when my alarm went off the following morning at 6am sharp.

I was back at the bubble wrap factory, the same place I'd been purposely fired from six months prior. Even by my standards, this job was boring. It consisted of a long row of boxes containing tiny strips of bubble wrap, and a desk in front of me that had two lines drawn with a permanent marker 20cm apart. My job was to take strips of bubble wrap from the boxes on my left and measure them one by one. Then divide them up, strips smaller than 20cm in one box and strips bigger in another. I was situated alone at the back of the factory, with no one to talk to, not even a radio for company. The last time I was here was straight off the back of a particularly heavy night and basically, I couldn't give a toss. I crawled into one of the boxes, surrounded myself with bubble wrap, and fell into a deep, comfy sleep. I woke up only when the factory manager started kicking the fuck out of the box and screaming at me about disrespect, my bad attitude and what have you. I crawled slowly out of the box, smiled at matey-boy and walked out of the factory. The same dude was there to meet me that morning. He was about to give me some kind of talking to, he strutted right up, all big-chested and blustered, but when he saw the look in my eye, it seemed to unnerve him. He simply said, "No funny business!" and sloped off to manage the bubble wrap needs of East Anglia.

All-day I dreamed about robbing Tescos - hypothetically of course - ways in which Dave and I would outsmart Sheila and drive off into the sunset, with half a million quid in cash money. It's probably worth mentioning that this was in 1999. Credit and debit cards existed, but not like they do now. Nobody really used them - well, especially not Essex housewives doing the weekly shop; they all paid in cash. Low denomination, untraceable cash. Most of the daydreams were like Hollywood movies, us blasting in there and shooting the place up with machine guns while shouting "Gimme all the cash!" at the frightened cashiers. Fun to think about, but not very realistic. Either way, the daydreams stayed with me, planning exit strategies and even planning speeches I'd be giving to a supermarket full of customers face down on the floor in front of me. I had plenty of time to think; the bubble wrap didn't really need me after all.

After work, my mate Stretch came to pick me up. It was a Friday, and my folks were out of town for the weekend. My brother had recently moved out of the house, meaning I had the place to myself, a rare occasion that wasn't going to go to waste. Dave was heading into town with a girl he was seeing at the time, but Stretch and a few others were coming over to mine for a smoke. He picked me up out front of work in his white transit van, Mickey Finn *Fantazia* rave tapes blaring out of a tiny sound system that wasn't doing the tunes or the speakers any favours whatsoever. It did seem to piss off matey-boy though, so again I gave him a smile and went on my merry way, chucking my BMX in the back of the van and screeching off into the sunset. Or back to my house in Rayne, a small village just outside of Braintree town.

Stockley and Gina were sitting outside my house when we arrived back. Both were school friends, Mudhills Crew. Stockley had brought along a teenth of hash, and our faithful pipe the Miller (made at School in Mr Miller's class), and Gina had brought a bottle of MD20/20. Thinking back now, it's strange, but I can't recall how we used to communicate with each other back then. Only a few of us had mobiles, and they were used for playing *Snake* more than practical arrangements, but everyone always seemed to know where and when we'd be hanging out. Free houses didn't come around that often, but when they did everyone descended on them. We'd usually spend our nights at the steps down Rayne Park or at the Mudhills, which was practically a ditch on the outskirts of Braintree Town, so the comfort of a house, free of parents, was a godsend. This rarely happened at my house. Sure, my parents went away a fair bit. But as I said, my brother had only just moved out, so anytime my folks went away, my house belonged to my brother and his mates, not me and mine. Now it was my turn, so it came as no surprise when Stockley told me that Clare and Jo were also on their way over.

I was in love with Clare; she was incredible. She was wild and up for anything, full of life and smiles, and as pretty as the flower in her hair. We'd been on-and-off and off-and-on for the past few months. At present we were off, for reasons I can't recall, but I was happy she was coming. She and her pal Jo were thick as thieves and always up to something. Stockley and Gina were also probably an item, although neither of them would admit it. Stockley was a small kid with a big personality. He was pretty crazy and lived by his own set of rules; he and Dave had grown up around the corner from each other, and he was now a good mate of mine. I guessed he'd be staying the night, which was fine by me. I was pretty sure that Bluey and Jot would also turn up at some point, both being from Rayne. Bluey had gone to a different school from the rest of us, a grammar school. He was a smart kid, much smarter than me. We'd become friends as kids in the village and bonded over a love of computer games. Bluey had an Amiga 500, and we'd spend countless hours in his room playing *Sensible Soccer* and *IK+*. Bluey and Jot also brought some more things to drink and smoke. Stretch had brought with him his collection of films on VHS. It wasn't the most extensive collection - in fact, it was only two films. *Boyz in the Hood* and *Point Break*. The plan for the night was to get fucked up and watch the movies, even though we'd all seen them hundreds of times already. Things were different in the '90s. This was standard behaviour.

OK, maybe I'd not seen *Point Break* hundreds of times, but I'd seen it a lot. Like maybe 20 times. But watching it that night was different. With half my mind running through ways to rob Tescos, the film took on a whole new purpose. If you've not seen it then you should: a Keanu Reeves and Patrick Swayze classic, with Keanu as a high flying FBI agent tracking down a crew of bank robbers called the Ex-Presidents, who dress up as American presidents and rob banks around California. The crew turn out to be super cool surfer dudes who rob the banks so they can live the dream and stick it to the man, not hurting anyone on the way. Or at least that's the plan, but shit hits the fan, people get hurt or die - it's Hollywood after all. It ends in a big showdown where Swayze disappears under a giant wave, meaning he never gets caught. It's excellent because the robbers in the film are the good guys, or at least you want to be them. Certainly Stretch did; he considered himself a surfer. Even though he'd only actually been out on a surfboard twice in his life, he knew that's what he wanted from life, like it was hard-wired into him. His dream was to live in Australia or New Zealand and ride the waves.

Later in the evening, Dave came by, his night out in town being cut short for some reason or another. Little did we know it then, but that night would become symbolic for everything that went down. Those nine people ended up being our crew, our Ex-Presidents. Dave arrived shortly after the end of the film, and we'd started chatting with the gang about our plans to rob the Tescos where Dave worked. Please be aware, this was still 100% hypothetical; we just talked and joked about the subject. Everyone had ideas to throw in. By Bluey's calculations there would be even more money held at a Tesco than we'd initially thought. Bluey also had ideas of what you'd do with the money after the robbery to keep it safe and make it clean. Stockley and Gina had some pretty exciting ideas on how to control the staff and customers in the shop, and Stretch knew the quickest way to get the fuck out of there. We talked through the night, sat around my parent's dining room table, making notes, drawing maps and putting together a plan. Come sunrise, fresh out of booze and smoke, including the entire contents of my parent's drinks cupboard, it felt like we'd covered everything, thought out each angle of this crazy idea. Still just a crazy idea though, right? That time of the morning came when the room's mood changed, and everybody knew it was time to head home (or head to bed in my case). Like the flicking of a switch, that was the end of the night. But before people started making their excuses, Clare stood up at the table and said, "I think we should do it. Fuck it. I'd do anything to get out of Braintree. What have we got to lose?" Then she left the room, went upstairs and got into my bed. Looks like we were back on. Hallelujah.

The next night, all nine of us met up at the Wetherspoons in town. Usually, we'd be up and about socialising with mates or other people, getting pissed on cheap pints. But instinctively, the nine of us found a spot at the back of the pub, huddled around the table, and began chatting about the plan again. Everyone had been thinking about it nonstop, and had lots more ideas, new strategies to think about, and new obstacles to consider. That's how it went down for the next six months. Where exactly we crossed the line from stoners to criminals I'm not sure; it was a slow process. But we all worked on the plan in every available hour, at each other's houses, down the pub, down the Wreck, doing recon missions to Tesco, and Dave working it from the inside, gathering information. By December 1999, we were ready to execute. It was on.

At the end of the millennium, the world lost its shit. Well, certainly the Western world anyway. Everybody knows you're supposed to have a good time on New Year's Eve. Celebrations are supposed to be easy, and that was never a problem before, but in the build-up towards the year 2000, things got stupid. People's collective anxiety about trying to have the time of their lives collided with opportunist greed from pubs, clubs and restaurants. It sent ticket prices through the roof and actual chances of enjoying yourself to a new low. There was a conspiracy theory about a mass computer breakdown called the Y2K bug, which could potentially make any or every computer act irrationally. That, coupled with cheap fireworks being sold by the bucketload and booze by the truckload, and the whole Millenium celebration was on course to be quite the fiasco. People were more anxious than ever, and what do people do when they're anxious? They shop. Tesco was also closed for a 'shock horror' two days over New Year's Eve and New Year's Day, causing even more panic for the good people of Great Notley Garden Village: they would have to stockpile. Takings at Tesco before all this went down were set to be at an all-time high, making Thursday 30th December the perfect day for us to execute our plan.

That morning we all met at the Mudhills for one last session before showtime. I wasn't nervous in the slightest, I was buzzing: so excited it's hard to explain. I'm confident to say everyone else felt the same too; this was one of the many things we'd spoken about in-depth in the lead-up. Our mental state on the day was critical. We needed to be confident and in a good place. We knew there was no room for error, we expected changes to the plan that would make us think on our feet, and we'd planned for that, but we weren't just intending to get away with this, we were planning to nail the fucking thing, smash it out the park, do it in style and love every minute of it. To me it felt like the biggest gig I was ever going to play, and if you're going to do a good gig, you don't just enjoy it, you love it. You own it. That was the plan. We'd need to tune into the nerves and ride them. There wasn't actually anything to be said or done that morning at the Mudhills as everything was in place, but it was essential that we saw each other. We smoked one last lung and went separately back to our houses, knowing full well that whatever happened, we'd never smoke at the Mudhills ever again. The sight of nine teenagers coming out of a bush on the edge of Braintree Town was nothing new and would turn no heads; we'd been smoking in that spot since we were 15 years old, it looked normal. We almost wanted to be seen, one of the many plans we had to throw anyone off our scent come tomorrow, when the news hit.

I walked home, down the old railway track that ran between Braintree and Rayne, cleverly named 'the Track', thinking about saying farewell to my parents. They'd been good to me, and I was going to miss them. I knew I'd be able to see them again once the dust had settled, and for now, they were none the wiser about what was about to go down. I did plan on telling them, but not until we were long gone. I'd probably call them once we were set up and safe in California. I didn't ever see them suspecting us either, even when they heard news of the robbery. I'd told them the same thing that we'd told Jot and Dave's folks and anyone else that would listen. Jellicoe had a big New Year's gig in Berlin, we'd be hunted down by a big European record label who wanted to break the band on the continent, kicking off with this show. Completely fabricated of course, but somewhat believable to our folks and the rest of our friends and families. We even got the news into the Braintree and Witham Times who ran a "local band does good" column. Everyone believed us; we said they were paying for our travel, and we could also bring Stockley and Gina along as crew. The imaginary tour lasted the whole of January, so when we all vanished after the robbery, no one would think to link it to us. My plan was to call home three weeks in and say we'd be given the chance to record and tour in America and would be leaving indefinitely. Clare and Jo were going to act as if they decided to join us last-minute on a whim (nothing new there), and Bluey and Stretch had their own plans and alibis in place. There was no reason anyone would tie us nine teenagers to this robbery. If you knew us, you'd know this was not the sort of thing we'd be into at all. A bunch of grebo stoners, never causing any trouble, one look at us and you'd know we were not criminal masterminds - this was all part of the masterplan.

I kept my farewells with my folks short, so they wouldn't suspect anything. They knew full well I was itching to get out of the house and into the big wide world, they'd known it for a while, and fully encouraged it. In my room, I packed my bag. I had a brand new suitcase, much larger than I'd ever usually travel with, and inside I put one change of clothes, much less than I would usually travel with. The remaining space was, of course, for the cash. We all had new suitcases. All of them from Tesco. Everything we were using for the robbery that we couldn't source for free we'd bought from Tesco. Not necessarily the Great Notley store, we'd spread it out, sometimes needing to travel to larger stores in Basildon and Chelmsford for particular items. We'd also spread the purchases out over the past few months. Each time we realised we needed something, we went out and bought it. Doing this meant it was basically untraceable to us. Coming from Tesco, each item would be cheap and extremely common, so it wouldn't stand out. It was a good idea, but it also had a poetry to it. Knocking off Tesco with equipment bought solely from Tesco was poetic, and if we were going to get away with this, we'd need poetry on our side. Tesco had everything we needed, everything that is, apart from the gun. Stockley sourced that.

Stretch picked me up at 6pm on the dot, we drove to pick up Dave and headed down the Wreck, where we all got changed into our red overalls with our black rucksacks. We kept our gloves and balaclavas to hand, but wouldn't actually put them on until we were just outside the store. Stretch rolled his balaclava up like a woolly hat and slipped a high-vis waistcoat over his jumpsuit. We also sprayed some mud up the sides of the transit and covered both front and back plates, making them unidentifiable. Then Stretch sprayed the plates with hairspray. An old wives tale says that it reflects the light and makes them unreadable to security cameras. I didn't believe that for a minute, but it couldn't hurt, so it'd been done. Now the plates were muddy and unrecognisable to anyone. The van would only be in sight of three cameras in the next three hours anyway, and after that, it would vanish with the rest of us.

It's hard to put my finger on exactly what I hated about Great Notley Garden Village. Construction had begun on the edge of town about six years beforehand. I guess the location was chosen due to its proximity to Stansted Airport, 20 minutes door to door, all thanks to the new bypass around Braintree that was part of the massive airport expansion. Great Notley Garden Village currently had around 700 houses and counting, each house had a slightly different look to it, even though they were all fundamentally the same. The whole thing was connected by roundabouts, speed bumps and well-lit suburban streets that ended in stupidly named cul-de-sacs. But that wasn't it. The problem I had was its forced character and complete lack of soul. It just felt and looked pretend, like it wasn't real life but some imaginary version of life. Annoyingly harmless. Simultaneously, on the other side of town, Braintree Freeport was thrust into existence, a hellish shopping centre for big brands and chain shops. It was so fucking polished, so sterile. Perhaps I was just scared? Scared I'd end up working at the Adidas shop in Freeport and living in Great Notley Garden Village forever. Maybe it was just teenage angst? Rebelling against the perfectly good life that was placed in front of me. Perhaps I was jealous? These kinds of houses were more than my folks could afford. I honestly can't remember exactly how I felt, but I can remember that I hated it. It smelt of bullshit and corporate ownership. Like a farm for humans, building lives built around shopping. Because slap bang in the middle of Great Notley Garden Village's modern circular layout, at the beating heart of it all, was Tesco.

7:30pm

Stretch pulled up and dropped Dave and I directly outside Tescos main entrance, our balaclavas now down, we jumped out of the van. Waiting outside were Stockley and Clare, both dressed in Santa outfits. Yes, Christmas was five days beforehand, but we'd decided it was an excellent collective disguise, because you could cover your full face without raising suspicion. Apart from me, Dave and Stretch, everyone else had walked to Tesco from home, putting on their Santa disguises at a suitable point on the way. Everyone had matching red jumpsuits, black gloves, shoes and rucksacks. Underneath the Santa hats and beards were black balaclavas, ready to be pulled down. We were all in matching uniforms, and we looked like we meant business. Which of course we did.

7:31pm

Dave and I walk through the door, followed closely by Stockley. Dave closed and locked the automatic front doors with a key that he'd obtained. This was the only public entrance to the store, while Stockley and I moved straight to Sheila at her security station just inside of the door. Before she had a chance to look up, Stockley drew the gun and held it directly between her eyes, while I calmly asked her to take a step back. Then I stood between her and the emergency alarm button and explained the situation.

"Good evening Sheila, we're here to rob Tesco. We have no intention of hurting you or anybody else. But we will if we need to. It's not your money, it's all insured, so just shut the fuck up and do exactly as I say."

I said all this in a thick Geordie accent, something I'd been practising since we came up with the idea. We decided that in any conversation during the robbery we'd all talk in Newcastle accents, thereby throwing people off the scent and causing confusion. Every meeting we'd had for the last two months had been in character; we'd picked it up from *Byker Grove* and all sounded legit. We also decided that once in the store, we'd all call each other Sheila, so as not to mistakenly call out someone's real name, but also to add confusion into the situation - especially for the head of security, whom we needed to be compliant and confused. That said, we had full intention of keeping speech to an absolute minimum.

7:32pm

Clare had stayed outside the store entrance. She removed the beard, but kept the wig and the Santa hat. Her face was exposed, but she knew not to look up where the CCTV would see her. She held a clipboard to give her a sense of authority, and wore a Tesco staff badge, Dave having secured a few of these before he'd left. For the next ten minutes, she'd be apologising to people trying to enter the store claiming that a computer malfunction on the tills meant that the store had to close early and wouldn't be open now until the 2nd of January. "The Y2K bug? Who knows?" But she passed on Tesco's sincerest apologies, wished everyone a happy new year, and suggested they try Tescos in town.

We knew that people wouldn't be leaving the store as we entered; Bluey was in charge of that. He was already inside when we'd arrived, dressed as Santa. Anyone trying to leave the store was stopped by him offering free gifts, making sure we had a clear run in.

7:33pm

Jot and Jo were also inside the store, and along with Bluey they now pulled down their balaclavas from inside their Santa outfits, removed their weapons from their rucksacks and took their positions. Stockley, Sheila and I went to the cigarette kiosk at the front of the store. This also acted as a kind of front desk and had the microphone for the store tannoy. On Shelia's instruction, the chap working behind the desk handed me the microphone and stepped out, I jumped onto the counter where I'd be visible, and hit the button.

DING-DONG.

"This is a customer announcement: this supermarket is being robbed. The doors are locked. We don't want to hurt you, but we will if we need to. We have weapons, and we don't give a fuck. So do exactly as we say. This will be over in exactly 12 minutes."

7:34pm

Dave, Jot, and Bluey shot the flamethrowers into the air in unison and patrolled across the front of the store. Of course, they weren't actual flamethrowers, they each had a disposable plastic lighter and a can of Lynx Africa, but after much practice, they knew how to create quite the spectacle. The cans were doctored to let out more of the best selling body spray than usual, so it was a big flame. Loud too.

7:35pm

"Every customer in the store is now asked to move towards the back of the store immediately."

Like sheepdogs, Jot and Bluey ran up each aisle herding the customers, beginning at the tills and pushing them towards the back of the store. Flamethrowers blazing, nobody kicked up a fuss, they all moved obediently. At the back of the store, they were met by Jo, and she instructed them to get into the walk-in storage freezer. It was a big fucking freezer, big enough to hold at least 60 people in relative comfort, which we'd guessed would be enough. Turns out that day there were 47 customers in the store at the time of the robbery, so plenty of room. Of course, it was cold, so Jo turned the freezer off once everyone was locked inside. They wouldn't be in there for long, and that many people would warm it up a bit, so nobody was in danger. It was the perfect place to get everyone out of our way as there was no mobile phone signal inside, but more importantly, you could lock it from the outside. Any staff members from the aisles or the meat and fish counter at the back were also locked safely away. We were, of course, keeping busy at the front of the store too.

7:36pm

"Every staff member on a checkout, please take out your till and bring it to the end of your conveyor belt. Immediately."

I jumped off the counter, went behind the kiosk desk and removed the till while Dave started moving precisely through the store with a Tescos shopping trolley, instructing each checkout assistant to place their tills in the trolley then to lay face down on the floor. Each till quickly unclipped from the checkout as a neat metal box, full of cash. All staff members did as they are told without any fuss. Perhaps because he was followed by Stockley, with his gun pointed at the back of Sheila's head.

7:37pm

Out of nowhere, a staff member shouts hysterically and runs towards Stockley and Sheila, without hesitation, and before she gets too close, Stockley swiftly moves the gun from behind Sheila's head and shoots the woman in the leg.

BANG.

It's fucking loud. The woman's knee explodes, blood goes everywhere, she hits the floor screaming. Her hands move between her knee and her face, covering her face in blood. It's a horrific sight, she screams uncontrollably, then passes out and goes silent.

"We apologise for any inconvenience caused. But I did warn you," I say into the microphone. The mood in the room had changed, as we knew it would. We now have full control and everyone's undivided attention.

7:38pm

Dave collected each of the ten tills, bringing him, Stockley and Sheila to the far side of the store and the entrance of the 'staff only' door. At this point, I jump down and run over to join them. Dave then keeps watch over the staff while Stockley and I proceed to the money room.

When a till gets full of cash, the staff member on duty puts up a little 'till closed' sign up and does a 'money drop'. It's called that even though the money actually goes up. The cash is neatly placed into a plastic pod, inserted into a tube no bigger than a drainpipe and, using compressed air, it is fired upward into an intricate set of tubes that take the money away, never to be seen again. Or so the staff are told, anyway. Truth is, it gets fired to the money room. Dave had been doing some gentle reconnaissance on the money room since day one. It was pretty easy to befriend Grant, who worked in there. We were never sure of his actual job title, and Dave didn't dig too deep, just ate lunch with him from time to time and let him do the talking. In short, the room was staffed by one person at a time whose job was to count the money and have it packed and prepared for collection. We also knew that Grant had two young kids and lived on the Fairview estate. Of course, the room was heavily locked, needing a key on the inside and outside of the door. It was rigged with emergency buttons that would inform the police directly. Plus it had CCTV at every angle. We knew all of this; we also knew that the main shop tannoy came into the room, meaning that Grant (whom we knew was working that day) would be fully up to speed with what was going down.

7:39pm

BANG BANG BANG.

I knocked on the door as hard as I could

"Grant Farrow. We're outside the door. We have a gun pointed at Sheila's head. We know you've pressed the emergency button, don't worry about that. We also know that little Danny and Tracy are at home with mum at the Fairview estate, we know all sorts of things about you. Sheila has her key inserted on this side of the door we now need you to..."

Before I'd finished the sentence, the key was in, and the door was opened. The three of us piled into the room, Stockley moved the gun from Shelia and now pointed it directly at Grant.

I thanked Grant for his understanding and instructed him and Sheila to give me their keys and lay face down on the floor.

7:40pm

Bluey arrived outside the room with two shopping trolleys. He and Stockley started to fill them up. The money was expertly packed into bags, and there were shit-loads of them, filling two trolleys-full. I used the phone in the money room and dialled the SECOM switchboard. SECOM was the security company that looked after this and all the other Tescos in the country. They installed the alarm system, the CCTV and managed their emergencies. I knew this because my old man was a SECOM employee; unbeknownst to my dad, he'd been an essential piece of the puzzle. We'd done a couple of trips to Tesco with me asking him questions about work, where the CCTV would go, how the footage would be stored and so on. He'd told me about the silent alarms, (which were no doubt going off) and the process that happens in the event of an emergency. The silent alarms go to the SECOM switchboard, and they call the police.

7:41pm

While dialling the number, I asked Grant for the SECOM access code, which he gave up without any protest. I gave the access code to the representative on the other end of the phone and said we'd been having some kind of computer malfunction throughout the store. They told me that the silent alarm had been triggered several times (sneaky Shelia must have hit it as we entered) and the police were on their way. I said there was no need for police, but we would need an engineer as soon as possible. "Maybe it was the Y2K bug?" Then I hung up. Of course, I knew this wouldn't stop the police from coming - no doubt they were on their way already, and would for sure need someone to check it out. Stretch was out front dealing with that, it was all in hand. But some more confusion thrown into the mix was only going to benefit us during our escape.

7:42pm

I joined Dave and Jo back on the shop floor while Stockley and Bluey finished loading the trolleys and then locked Sheila and Grant in the money room. Everything on the shopfloor was in order.

7:43pm

"Shelia, we're out of here!" I shouted. Upon hearing this code, Gina stood up from the floor. Her face was still covered in tomato soup. She'd been the first of us all to enter the shop that day, wearing a full Tesco uniform that Dave had swiped. She'd milled around the shop waiting for her moment, then screamed and ran towards Stockley. Of course, we had no intention of shooting anyone, but we knew creating that idea would benefit us. Stockley's gun was a BB gun, very popular at the time and readily available in lots of creepy shops that also sold crossbows, knives and karate kits. Stockley never actually divulged where he'd got it from, but he promised it was untraceable. It was made of metal and looked and felt legit. We'd painted over the red plastic on the inside of the barrel, and even used fireworks to give the gun a used gunpowder smell. I'd also used a firework to create the gunshot sound - while all eyes were trained on Stockley, I'd been behind the desk at the cigarette kiosk. I turned the tannoy's volume to the maximum and let a firework off directly into the microphone. We'd gone on the assumption that nobody who was in the store would actually know what a real-life gunshot sounded like. We didn't even know what the firework would sound like down the tannoy, but fucking hell it worked. It was crazy loud and rang out throughout the whole store at top volume. The slight gunpowder smell in the room added to the effect, at the same time Gina used a fork in her hand to break a balloon full of tomato soup beneath her already-ripped trousers and started to scream in pain. It was an act that they had worked on religiously, it was seamless, beautiful; back at school Gina would have received an A for drama GCSE, maybe even an A+. Before she faked passing out, she covered her face in the soup, meaning that her face was now concealed from staff, customers and cameras. On cue, she stood up, and we all made our way to the back of the store.

7:44pm

The seven of us left via the loading bay. I was the last out of the door and shouted, “Thank you for shopping at Tesco!” before throwing one more firework into the store, just to keep the staff in place. The van was waiting in the dock, back doors wide open. Stretch at the wheel and Clare in the passenger seat. We piled into the back of the van, once we’d loaded the three trolleys full of cash.

7:45pm

We all climbed in and slammed the doors as Stretch calmly drove away. While we’d been inside, Stretch had been busy. His first move had been to drive out of the Tesco car park and close the exit to the car park behind him - that was easy enough. Donning his high visibility vest, he’d simply pulled the barricades they use during closing hours and sealed them with a brand new padlock, locking all the cars inside. He was wearing a Tesco staff badge, and he’d apologised to a few customers in their vehicles, saying there was some kind of issue on the bypass and they’d been asked to close the exit and that it would be open again very shortly. He’d then walked back to the van, removed a ‘ROAD CLOSED’ sign and four traffic cones, and shut off the exit to the roundabout. He’d directed a few cars back the way they came and then closed the other exit, again giving vague apologies to the drivers at the barricades, this time saying there had been an incident in Tescos. He’d then got back in the van, and driven back in through the entrance to Tescos car park, jumped out of the van and padlocked the entrance gate behind him. A quick scan of the skyline confirmed what we knew would happen: absolute gridlock in all directions. People were being generally calm though, confused more than anything else; few angry horns, but that was about it. The roads leading in from both directions were dual carriageways, no hard shoulder, and they were backed up within minutes. Backed up all the way to other roundabouts and other roads. The whole area was locked down, and nobody knew why. By the time anyone dared to remove the signage, we'd be long gone, and the lack of hard shoulder meant there was no way the police could get through to either find out what was going on with the traffic or to find out that Tescos was being robbed.

Stretch jumped in the van, swung by the front of the store to collect Clare, and then drove around the back to the loading bay. Obviously, Stretch and Clare were both in disguise. They're the only two who'd been seen by the general public and caught from a bad angle by a piss poor security camera. Nonetheless, everyone in town knew Stretch, for his silly dreadlocks, and Clare because she was so fun and so wild. So Stretch had shaved his dreads that morning, wore a pair of glasses rather than his usual contact lenses, and had a woolly scarf around his neck: he looked nothing like Stretch. Clare had been dressed as Santa, or Mrs Santa, with a hat, clip-on elf ears and a scarf pulled up high.

The service entrance to Tesco was unaffected by the traffic chaos as it was on the other side of the store and unknown to the public. We slowly rolled out of Great Notley Garden Village without any fuss whatsoever. Stretch knew precisely what was going on in the back of the van and drove calmer and slower than he had ever driven before so we could change clothes and re-distribute the money. All of the roads surrounding Tecos and Braintree were gridlocked; all except for the one road out that existed before the bypass, before the shopping centre and before Tesco popped its big arse down in the middle of it, the good old B1256. It connected Great Notley to Stansted from days of old. All around was indescribable traffic chaos, but the B1256 was as empty as a bottle. We knew it would be; remember, this was a time before Sat Navs, let alone Google Maps, the idea of a computer being able to tell you where a traffic jam was forming was unfathomable, so everyone just drove onto the shiny new bypass and got locked in while we slowly ambled off up the country road. A short drive too, 20 minutes later and we were at Bishop Stortford Train Station.

Stretch dropped us off in our travel groups, undetected at the back of the train station car park, out of sight from any of the station's four cameras. Clare and Jo got out first. Both now wearing wigs and dressed in two-piece business suits, each with a roller suitcase rammed with cash. They went straight to the station entrance and boarded the shuttle bus that ran between the station and Stansted airport every 30 minutes. Once they were clear, Gina and Stockley did the same. They were dressed up like they were going out for a nice meal, and playing the happy couple. They got the bus after Clare and Jo. Bluey was the only one who boarded a train, he had the bulk of the cash on him, two of the biggest roller suitcases we could find in Basildon Tesco. He was getting the train to London, the Eurostar to Brussels and then to Switzerland via Köln in Germany, taking the long way around to throw anyone off the scent. Still, no doubt he'd be in Zurich long before any of us arrived at our destination.

Dave, Jot and I waited for the next shuttle bus as Stretch left with the van. He drove it to a spot ten minutes away that we'd scoped out in advance, a discrete farmers road on the edge of Hatfield forest that led to a large travellers site. He parked the van, left the keys in the ignition and got out of there, carrying his huge 'I'm travelling the world!' backpack. Rather than having gap-year essentials, it was obviously rammed with cash. I always found the local travellers sites fascinating, completely mysterious. I knew so little about their way of life, but I was confident that the van would be gone in no time, never to be seen again. Hopefully, they'd find a use for the trollies we left in the back of the van too.

Dave, Jot and I didn't have to don a costume as such, we were 'the band'. As well as the roller suitcases, we also had guitar, bass and drum cases, rammed with cash, as much as the three of us could carry. The plan for everyone was to check the money bags in at the gate. We'd counted out £2,000 each to keep on our persons and take on the flight; to us it was a tremendous amount of money, but in the wider world not really enough to raise any eyebrows. If questioned, it fitted into our travel stories anyhow. Ours, for example, was a gift from the record label we'd signed to. Cash payouts to new bands were a thing back then, even if it sounds nuts now. The lion's share of the cash would be checked in at the gate, and this was the biggest question mark hanging over the whole shenanigans. This was the bit we had no control over at all. We'd done the best research that we could, looking into how and when baggage is scanned and what the scanners might be looking for. The cash wouldn't show up in the X-ray, and we'd packed it all keeping the shape of the suitcases and thrown in some toothpaste and shoes to hopefully make the scans look a bit more normal. Most of the X-raying would be done in foreign countries anyhow, and even if we got caught, linking us to Great Notley Tescos wasn't a given anyway. This was the unknown, but a risk we'd all been willing to take.

At least it was the biggest unknown until I saw Steph at Takeley train station. The minute that I saw her, I knew exactly what was happening. I looked at Jot. "You're not coming?" I said, and he shook his head. Jot and Steph had met at college, and in the short time that we'd been planning the robbery they had fallen head over heels in love. I'd had an uneasy feeling from Jot in the last few weeks, but decided to ignore it, but now it made sense. "I love you guys," Jot said. "And I wanted to go ahead with the robbery as planned, because I believed in it and knew that we could do it, but me, personally I don't wanna get the fuck out of Braintree, that was never my plan. I like it here. I want to stay with Steph, raise a family and be near my family." It was a fair point "I'll take my cut of the cash, I'll go back to my mum and dad's and doss about for a year or so before I even think about spending a penny. I'll keep your alibi strong and just tell everyone I left the band before you left for Germany. No reason anyone will suspect us." My mind was racing. "I can also act as a man on the ground; who knows, if the dust settles, you can probably even come back at some point."

There was no time to overthink it, and Jot had clearly made up his mind. Fair play to him, we hugged it out, him and Steph went to get the train back to Braintree, and Dave and I boarded the bus to the airport.

Once at the airport, we did the same as the others had done before us, went to the desk and booked tickets for a flight that left in an hour, didn't matter where so long as we were all on different flights leaving at different times. Dave and I booked onto a flight to Reykjavík in Iceland, leaving at 10pm. We didn't see any of the others in the airport; to be honest, we weren't sure when we'd ever see them again - probably not for some time. Stretch would be the last to arrive at the airport, where he would travel solo to New Zealand, and Bluey was planning on losing himself around Europe for a while before heading out to Hong Kong. In Reykjavík airport, Dave and I changed our £2,000 each into dollars and booked a flight to LA.

We glided through LAX with ease, stopping briefly at border control, where we said we were young musicians with money in the bank who'd come to spend it in America with the hope of making the big time. With the click of a stamp, we were granted a 6-month stay in the country, plenty of time. Our roller bags and guitar cases were waiting patiently for us at the carousel when we arrived, untouched and apparently unnoticed. We grabbed them and, heads down, jumped in a cab.

With a bit of bartering, the cab driver helped us score some weed, which was incredibly easy. He also helped us find some rolling tobacco, which was almost impossible, but we found it. Then he dropped us off at a Diamond White second-hand car dealership. We'd chosen this one as it shared a name with our tipple of choice down Rayne Park. We purchased a blue Ford Mustang, named it 'Sunshine The Second', and Dave drove it to Griffith Observatory while I skinned up in the glove compartment.

By now, Bluey would have deposited the main haul of the cash into a Swiss bank account in our individual names. We needed to find a computer somewhere where he'd set us up something called an email, we'd be able to access this from any computer and get the account details needed to wire the cash whenever we wanted it. But that could wait, now we just had to sit back and watch the sunset over LA and smoke some of the best weed we'd ever smoked. We'd done it. Nobody had been hurt, nobody had been caught, nobody was chasing us or even suspected us. Six months in the making, 48 hours to execute. When that sun rose the following morning, it would be 1st January 2000. The beginning of a new millennium. We had a car full of cash, money in the bank, friends on their way and our whole lives ahead of us. I passed the spliff to Dave, he took a long, thoughtful drag, held it for a second, then slowly and precisely blew the smoke out of the car window. Deep in thought, I could almost see the cogs turning as he looked me dead in the eye and said: "What have we got to lose?"

INTRO

OK, so that story was bullshit. Of course we didn't rob Tescos, let alone get away with it, but the bullshit tale was littered with truths. Yes, Dave did work in Great Notley Tesco while I worked in factories around Braintree. Yes, we used to sit in a car called Sunshine down the Wreck and smoke cheap hash, and yes we did talk in-depth about how to rob Tesco if we were so inclined. Most of the hair-brained ideas about the robbery and the getaway were devised 19 years ago as 19-year-olds. But we just weren't so inclined. At the time, we fantasised about writing it into a movie, or a song, neither of which happened (as of yet). So I went back through my memory, sharpened up a few points and bashed it out as the opening chapter, here in my new book.

I used it as the opening chapter hoping to suspend your disbelief. I doubt anyone believed that it went down like that, but all of the characters in the story are real friends of mine, and all the locations exist. Everything is based on truth apart from the robbery itself. Hopefully, you'll forgive the little white lie used to tell the story, mainly because I'd like you to believe that all the rest of the stories in this book are true. They all happened to me, and I intend to share them to the best of my ability and memory. Many of the stories take place alongside an embrace of hedonism, which has never been great for brain cells, but I'll do what I can.

I'm happy to say that even without the bags full of cash and the flights to California, Dave and I did get the fuck out of Braintree, moving to London at the same time the robbery was set. In the 20 years since, we were lucky enough to have lived the kind of lives that have incorporated dive bars of New York, LA sunsets, raving in Thailand, backpacking around India and bungee-jumping in New Zealand. We just managed it with cash we'd earnt rather than money we stole. The bungee-jumping was only a year ago. I was out in Queenstown to play a gig and visit Stretch, now a full New Zealand resident who runs a successful painting and decorating company in Queenstown.

I would imagine that if you're reading this, then you're already aware of who I am and what I do, but on the off chance that's not the case, by way of introduction, hello. My name is Beans on Toast. That's not true either, my real name is Jay McAllister, but I've been performing under the moniker of Beans on Toast for the last 15 years. I'm a songwriter, a folk singer and sometimes a storyteller.

This is my second book - my first, *Drunk Folks Stories*, came out in 2018. Like this book, that was a collection of stories about my life of touring, songwriting, drinking and blagging it. If you've not read the first book, fear not. They are not in chronological order and both are stand-alone reads. I might refer to the first book a bit in these pages where the stories overlap, but that's about it. For example, in my first book, there's a story called 'This is The Fish' where I talked about the punk rock-juxtaposed high jinx that is the Salty Dog Cruise. The next story in this book picks up where that left off, the Monday morning after the festival.

I never thought I'd write a book. It was never an ambition, never on my agenda or something that I pictured happening in my life. Much less that people would read it and (from the communication I've received back seemed to) enjoy it. The whole process was quite a surprise to me, so I thought I'd surprise myself again and write a second. The first book was written in 2017 in Germany. I was on an extended tour around the country, travelling alone on the Deutsche Bahn - or the train as I'd call it. Having four or five hours alone on a comfortable seat with my computer, I started to write down some stories I'd been telling for years. The experience of travelling back down memory lane was one I enjoyed. And the book, which I sold directly from my website and merch table at my gigs, was a hit. Not a hit in the sense of bestseller or award-winning or any benchmarks like that, but in my little world, it was a big deal, and I don't mind saying I'm very proud of it.

It seems this book will be conceived under very different circumstances, in the midst of a worldwide pandemic, locked down at home, gigs and tours cancelled for the foreseeable future and the system that we know so well slowly unravelling. The world-changing at such an incredible rate, I'd be stupid to pass comment on it here. No doubt post-lockdown, the world will be abundant with post-lockdown books, so you'll be pleased to hear this isn't one of those. No, I'll be venturing back into my past to try and throw up some fun stories, lessons learned, or bridges burned. I'll be honest and try to explain my thoughts and feelings on the events to the best of my ability. Before we get cracking, I just wanted to thank you in advance, even if you've only got this far and you're about to chuck the book out. Well, thanks for giving it a try. The world needs people to give things a try. That shit is important. You know what else is important? Telling the truth. So I wanted to throw this little intro in to let you know that the stories are all true from here on out. Promise.

THE KEY

Monday, 21st March 2016, 9:00am

Bang. Bang. Bang. It sounded like a cop knocking. I slowly came around, dazed, confused, but somewhat aware that the knocking and shouting had been happening for quite some time. "MR MCALLISTER!" came a shout from the other side of the locked door. "You are the last person to leave the boat. You must vacate your room immediately and take all your belongings with you. PLEASE."

Fuck. I sat upright and felt the full weight of a cruise ship squashing my brain to smithereens. I know some people who get really bad hangovers whenever they drink. I know people that don't get them ever. Me, I'm somewhere in the middle, leaning a bit towards the former as I get older. When I get them, I get them bad, and this morning it was worse than ever before. My head was in an awful place. I knew that instantly. A hangover like this was, of course, inevitable. I'd been to the Bahamas and back on a cruise ship with a free bar open 24 hours a day with nothing to do but play gigs, make new friends and hang out with old ones. It had been an epic few days of song, sand and punk rock.

Cruise ships are fucking weird places, a capitalist's dream and an environmentalist's nightmare. Gaudy and garish. Somehow tacky and lavish at the same time. Plonked right in the middle of the ocean and surrounded by empty beauty. A bizarre world isolated from everything else with the calm, mysterious sea as far as the eye can see in every direction. There is a glaringly obvious divide between the punters and the staff. I'd chatted with as many of the boat's crew as possible over the weekend - a mixed bag of people from all over the world. Everyone I spoke to enjoyed the job, some of them telling me that they live on the boat for up to a year at a time. Crazy. All of them said they were loving the Salty Dog Cruise, and attested it was like no other cruise they had ever worked on. Miguel also confirmed this. He'd been looking after the rooms in my corridor. We'd built a slightly awkward friendship over the last few days, me being drunk and him being helpful. It was him knocking and shouting from the other side of the door. I opened the door to see that the party was over. Miguel had had enough. I was being *that guy.* "Sorry mate, so sorry. I've been asleep. Give me two seconds."

I looked at all my stuff, evenly distributed around the room. Clothes, empty cans and dirty plates, it looked like the bedroom of a teenager. My guitar was out of its case, and half a box of merch had crash-landed in the corner of thc room. "I'll be as quick as I can, I promise Miguel." He nodded as I closed the door. Fuck. I started racing around the room, getting my shit together and trying to tidy up my mess. I stunk. One whiff of myself, and I nearly puked. I turned the shower on cold and stepped in.

I'm a big fan of a cold shower. If I can gather the courage to do it when I'm hungover, it usually works wonders. No such luck today though; the water hit me, and I broke into a shiver, almost passing out. No time for that now. I patted myself dry, threw on the cleanest Hawaiian shirt from my small collection and set off on my way. Between my guitar, my two bags and the merch, I had more than I could physically carry. No way I'd be able to get any help now, so I designed a technique of dragging the box behind me with the guitar on top, and rolling the bag with my other hand in front. It was clumsy at best. The hardest part, however, was carrying my head on my shoulders; it was getting heavier by the second.

I really was the last person off the boat. In my defence here, it was still before 10am on a Monday morning after a festival. I kind of remember people talking about an 8am check out, which seemed insane but turned out to be true, and they'd somehow managed it. The ship was empty, as was the check out area and border control. Even once I was off the boat, there wasn't a soul around. The car park was empty. Well, pretty much empty.

It was the only vehicle in the parking lot, obnoxiously parked diagonally across three parking spaces and surrounded by my friends, all looking very hungover and extremely concerned. The Bandwagon.

There are a few different ways to travel when you tour, starting on public transport and ending on a private jet. At the end of the day though, you'll be on the road at some point, and your choice of wheels will generally fall into two categories. The Tour Bus, or the Splitter. Say you're playing a run of shows to between 300 to 600 people a night. And say you have a band of six members and one or two crew (sound, merch and so on). You're on the fence, and you need to make a call. The more expensive option is to hire a tour bus. The bus comes with a professional driver, bunks, toilet, hang out spaces, and does wonders for the ego. The main benefit (aside from feeling like you're living out your childhood fantasies) is that you can sleep while you're moving. So you can do the gig, get pissed or do whatever you have to do, and as long as you're back on the bus by the 'bus call', you'll be waking up the next morning (or afternoon) parked outside the venue you're playing that night. The beds are like little coffins; you're pretty tightly packed in, but it's very comfortable. I've found the hum of the engine to be quite the lullaby, and have always slept soundly even though I knew in my heart I was hooning it down the motorway at 60 miles an hour without any kind of seat belt in place. That said, I don't think I've ever climbed into one of those coffins sober, so who knows?

The cheaper and less romantic way would be to travel by splitter. A splitter is a beefed up transit van that has been split into 2 compartments. The van's back half is for holding all the instruments and merch, always a tight fit, and it needs a Tetris mastermind to squeeze everything in. The front compartment has between six and ten seats, depending on your needs. Sometimes there's a table, a TV or some kind of games console. Generally quite comfortable, but nowhere to sleep, because if you're touring in a splitter, you'll also be staying in hotels. Meaning that after a gig, if you've got a long drive, you'd be looking at having to leave straight away, drive half the night, pull into a cheap hotel on the side of the road, cram the band and crew into as few rooms as possible (sharing beds is pretty much a given), get a few hours kip, then get up and back in the van the following morning to crack on with the rest of the drive. That is an extreme example, but it happens.

It certainly happened in the autumn of 2015 when I was on tour with Skinny Lister, the first time I'd met the band. I'd seen them play at Bestival a few years before. I absolutely loved them and was excited to finally meet them and to play some shows together. The tour was Frank Turner's North American run for his *Positive Songs for Negative People* album. I was opening, and Skinny were the main support. It was a mammoth run around the vast continent. 30 shows in 40 days, with drives that included the likes of Minneapolis to Denver (13 and a half hours) and Phoenix to Austin (15 hours) in the itinerary. The forms of touring that I've mentioned above don't really count for me. As a solo musician, my travel plans come together a lot easier. For tours like this, my first approach is always to see if I can ride with the band I'm supporting. I've travelled on Frank's tour bus many times, and kind of presumed that I'd be able to do that. It turned out his bus was full, but it had been arranged that I would travel with Skinny. As usual with this setup, you get a seat, you throw in for petrol and accommodation, and it works for everyone involved. I've done it with a few bands over the years, and it's always been a blast, but nothing has come close to what happened with Skinny.

Meeting someone for the first time knowing full well you'd be spending the next six weeks sitting next to them in a van and sharing dingy hotels with them has all the potential of being quite an awkward hello, but this was not the case. We hit it off, right off the bat. As I said, I was a fan of their music, which obviously helps. When I saw them at Bestival, I remember thinking how much fun they looked like they were having, and how I'd love to hang out with them. On meeting them, it felt like we'd been friends forever, and now, five years later, I can tell you that we will be. I fell in love with the whole band, each member having an array of different qualities off stage. And on stage they were able to blow the roof off night after night. If, for some crazy reason, you've not heard of the band, then do check them out. Sea shanties, accordions, dancing, crowd-surfing and drinking from the Sacred Flagon, you won't be disappointed. The band's core revolves around family. Lorna, the singer, stands side by side on stage with her husband Dan on guitar and her brother Max on accordion. There are things about being a solo musician that you miss out on compared to people in bands: the in-jokes, the camaraderie, the sounding board for ideas, and so on. On the road with them, I had all that. I pretty much joined the band. Joined the family.

That tour was in a splitter, with, as I said, some stupidly long drives and some ropey budget motels. In the van were the six members of Skinny, Jenna Lee on Merch, and myself. On tour, we co-wrote songs, left people in service stations, watched crap films, drank ourselves stupid, covered many miles, played some life-changing shows and generally had the time of our lives. Yes, Skinny know how to have a good time, but they also know how to tour. They're like a rock'n'roll machine. Each member is happy to take the wheel of the van, design the T-shirts, hang the backdrop or work the merch stand - whatever was needed, and everything was done with passion. While Dan was behind the wheel for a ten-hour straight drive, he'd be deep in a discussion about the setlist with the rest of the band, hoping to improve on it from the last gig. Lorna would be on the back seat, buried in a spreadsheet, trying to make the tour finances work for everyone. Obviously, in a perfect world, or to be honest, even a just world, then a band this great would have someone else to handle the tasks of tour management, driving and spreadsheets, but since that person wasn't there, the band did it themselves. They did it all for the music. They would do anything for the show, for the gig, for the songs. That was all that mattered, and that was why I loved them so much.

And there they were, next to the Bandwagon. Also dressed in bad Hawaiian shirts, no doubt also hungover to fuck, in the car park of the Port of Miami huddling around the massive, badly parked vehicle surrounded by luggage and instruments. I could feel the worry and confusion from across the carpark. I knew something was up.

On the last tour, we'd learnt a few things. Firstly that we loved touring together; it worked both on and off stage, and it was something both Skinny and I were keen to do more of. We also learnt that doing tours of America in a splitter van was near impossible; even for a band like Skinny it just didn't make sense. On the last tour, I'd started calling Dan 'D1000' because if the band were a rock'n'roll machine, then he was a rock'n'roll robot: smashing a set, packing the gear, driving all night and repeating the process. All he required was the audience applause and the odd chipotle burrito as fuel. It was impressive, but we knew that if we came back again to tour the States, we'd have to have a tour bus, so we could get some shut-eye while rolling down the highway. The only problem was we couldn't afford one.

And that is where the Bandwagon comes into play. A vehicle that doesn't exist on the UK touring circuit, I guess due to the country's size making it kind of redundant, the Bandwagon is smaller than a tour bus but bigger than a splitter. It has room for gear and seats, but also nine bunks and a rudimental toilet and shower. It is all stupidly compact, and housed in the back of what looks like a Winnebago owned by a retired Hell's Angel, black with silver trimmings. It sounded perfect. All of the tour logistics had been done in advance by Lorna, who was working on a shoestring budget. She had her concerns, I could tell, but nothing she wanted to get stuck into over the weekend. She was way too busy getting stuck into the free bar. The Bandwagon had been the talk of the town for us all weekend, checking out pictures online and getting excited for the tour that started when the festival finished.

Being as both Skinny and I had been lucky enough to score gigs on the Salty Dog Cruise, it made perfect sense for us to do a run of shows following the festival, and that was what had been arranged. Not the longest run with 10 shows in 13 days, but in that time, we'd be going as far north as Toronto. So, starting in Florida, we had a shit-ton of driving to do. The plan was to drive at night, in the Bandwagon, while we all slept. On paper, it was doable. I'd spoken to a bunch of American bands on the cruise about the Bandwagon, all bands that had now graduated to much more comfortable tour buses and not one of them had anything nice to say about it. It was known between musicians as the 'bone-rattler', and apparently, it's pretty shaky in the back at night. A few others professed they would never set foot in a Bandwagon again as long as they lived. I shrugged their warnings off. They can keep their fancy-pants tour buses. To me, it looked mint, and I couldn't wait to spend the next week rolling up the East Coast of the USA. I knew Skinny were buzzing too, and we'd all been looking forward to the big unveiling of the Bandwagon. So why all the long faces?

"What's going on?" I asked as I approached the throng. With each word, my hangover jumped up a level.

"We're locked out," said Will Varley.

Will is another dear friend and musical companion. Musically he does a similar thing to me, albeit a bit better. One man and guitar. Will has a truly beautiful voice, married with simple chords and songwriting that bores deep into your mind and your soul. He's one of my favourite songwriters, and that would stand true even if I didn't have the pleasure of being his friend. We first met at a show in Margate in 2013. The promoter of the show and an old friend, Dean Fragile, had put the gig together. At that time, I'd never heard of Will Varley, but a few people showed some excitement at us being on a bill together. I checked out his stuff a week before the show, as I generally do when sharing a bill. The first thing I watched was a live video of a song called 'These Are The Days', and I was instantly in love. I bought both of the albums he had out and completely devoured them in the lead up to the show. One week later, I knew all the words, and was more excited to see him play than I had been for any live gig for a long time. I saw him walking the streets of Margate on the afternoon of the show, and it got all Beatlemania. I shouted his name from across the road, and ran through passing traffic to hurriedly introduce myself. Will, in his usual calm manner, explained that we'd met before, a few times actually, and that he'd been in touch in the past about us playing shows together, but I hadn't got back to him. That says more about me than I'm probably willing to admit, but he found it funny and was clearly quite honoured that I'd now turned into a superfan. We went to the pub before our show that night, and our friendship began.

From what I can remember, that show in Margate was a bit of a mess - under-attended and pretty sloppy. I ended my show by coaxing Will to back up on stage to do a drunken rendition of 'American Pie'. I have no idea what I was thinking; it was obviously completely unrehearsed, as we'd only met that day, Will didn't know how to play it, and I didn't know the words. Still, it's funny, as it turns out Will and I did a fair bit of touring together in the States, so we'd often look back at that moment. After that gig, I invited Will to support me on my UK tour, which he did, and throughout that tour, we got to know each other, as is the way with tours. Since then, he's well outgrown the role of the support act. These days I'd support him. Not long ago, I saw him headline Shepherds Bush Empire. It was a beautiful thing. I've never seen this game as a competition and always want the best for my contemporaries. More power to him. Will had also done a tour with Skinny before the one we were all about to embark on. They too, then,were great pals. We were one big musical happy family about to hit the road and do what we love. So why all the long faces? What were we locked out of?

"I'm staying out of it," said Will. Clearly also hungover, he stepped out of the throng and into the small sliver of shade that the Bandwagon was providing from the hot-as-fuck beating sun. I turned back to the throng, where there was only one face that I didn't recognise. This was the face that looked the most worried. I leant in, put my hand out and said, "Hello mate, I'm Jay." He reached and shook my hand: "Foz."

Foz is the lead role of this story. His name isn't actually Foz. I've changed that for everyone's safety and security. My first impression of Foz was that he was a punk. And I don't mean that in a bad way. I consider myself part punk. It's a way of life that I can generally get behind, mainly due to the fact that punk is whatever you want it to be. Foz was a punk in a NOFX kind of way. He had spiked hair, a nose ring, tattoos all over the shop, wore grubby clothes over a skinny frame, and looked kind of spaced out - spaced out and worried.

"What's going on, Foz?" I asked.

Lorna jumped in, in full-on Mum mode. "Nothing to worry about, Jay. Foz here is our driver, and unfortunately, he managed to lock in the keys in the cab of the van when he arrived." Whoops. Apparently, after committing this awful parking atrocity, Foz had stepped out of the door, pressed down the lock and slammed it shut, thereby locking everyone out of the cab and the back part of the truck. Hence all the equipment and personal belongings of three musical acts were piled up around the Bandwagon in an empty parking lot. Just then, a few members of the port authority came over and told us to remove the vehicle. Lorna re-explained the situation to them, also adding in the news that a locksmith was on the way, but wasn't expected for well over an hour. There was nothing around but cruise ships we couldn't board and roads we couldn't drive on. No coffee shops or fast food joints where we could shelter from the sun or get refreshments. I joined Varley in the sliver of shade. "Not the greatest start," he said. No, but at least we didn't have a show that night.

See, this almighty hangover I was nursing was always part of the plan. It had been well prepared for in the organisation and routing of the tour. Today was a day off. We didn't have a show. The plan was to drive a short drive to Mark and Lindy's house in Tampa. They were friends of Skinny, they'd also been on the boat this weekend, and I'd hung out with them. Lovely couple. They promised a place to take a load off, some home-cooked food, a night off the booze and the banter and a decent night's sleep, probably not a bed for everyone, but enough room to make do. My hope was that we'd arrive mid-afternoon, get some lunch and then watch a film in silence, hopefully a rom-com. Maybe *Marley & Me*. That sounded like it'd do wonders for my hangover, but that dream was fading as fast as the sun was rising in the sky.

We sat in total silence for the next two and a half hours, waiting for the locksmith. I battered down my feelings of wanting to blame Foz for the whole scenario. I didn't know the chap, these things happen, we've all made stupid mistakes - I certainly have. So I convinced myself to give him the benefit of the doubt. The locksmith finally arrived and opened up the Bandwagon. The equipment quickly went into the back, and the nine of us stepped into what would be our home for the next ten days while we travelled 2,000 or so miles. It wasn't quite the fanfare I'd pictured when dreaming up the tour back in London. Moods and blood sugar levels were at an all-time low, and the hangovers were kept alive and kicking by the hot sun. It was hotter inside the Bandwagon than it was in the car park. The Bandwagon we'd seen on the website online was all new and shiny; this one was old and battered and cramped. As we piled in, it became apparent how little room we actually had. A quick head-count and scan of the seats made it clear that there weren't enough seats for everyone. I wasn't sure how that would even work. The seats it did have were not really seats either, more like a bench, going long-ways down the side of the van, not a seatbelt in sight. I kept my concerns to myself. I'm not one to complain, especially not complain about a tour of America. It was a tour bus, for fuck's sake. I was on tour. I should be over the bloody moon. I put it down to my hangover, and kept silent, threw my bag on one of the (tiny) bunks, took my place on the bench and put my head in my hands. Fuck, it was hot.

Shortly after that, the Bandwagon roared into action, and we bounced out of the parking lot. This was the first time we'd been out of earshot from Foz, and people had questions. Who was he? Where did we find him? How could he park the van so terribly? A tour bus driver's role is an odd one, mainly because it's detached from everyone else on the tour. They do their work while everyone else sleeps, and vice versa. On the tours I'd been on in the past, I'd found the drivers to be fascinating figures, generally of an older generation, wise and calm. To actually chat to them, you either had to stay up really late or get up really early. They obviously have a huge responsibility. In the past, every driver I'd met felt like a person who could handle that responsibility. I didn't want to admit it, but Foz wasn't really giving off that vibe. I didn't have to admit it though: everyone else asked the questions. They came raining down on Lorna as she quickly explained to everyone the reality of the situation. It's what we could afford. Professional tour drivers she's been put in touch with were out of our budget, and as a workaround, Lorna had found Foz on a Warped Tour chat room. I didn't even know Warped Tour was still a thing, let alone chat rooms. But apparently, they were. Foz had never driven a band on tour before, but he did have a full HGV license, and had worked delivering goods for a few years. He was a fan of Skinny Lister, wanted to start getting into band tour driving, and was willing to do it for a price that would work on our budget. Fair do's. My mind was kind of put to rest. He'd delivered goods, we were now the goods, we were in safe hands, that was fine. My head was still in my own hands at this point.

My head came out of my hands as my arse slipped off the bench and hit the floor. Max also fell off the bench, and bags and guitars toppled over and around. We'd apparently taken our first corner. It seemed somewhat dramatic, and the reality of a 2,000 mile drive became worryingly apparent. It also became clear just how cut-off we were from the driver's cab. Wanting some kind of recognition of the calamity that had just caught us all off-guard in the back of the van, Dan went to the small window that connected to the front. The only thing is that it wasn't connected at all. The driver's cab was a completely separate part of the vehicle. It also had a window, but between the two windows was a metre-wide gap,with the roar of the traffic between them. Dan banged out the window in our cabin but got zero response from Foz in the front. He had his eyes on the road, seemingly unaware of the chaos the corner had created in the back of the van. It was a weird feeling; a bad feeling. Being cut off from the front felt like we had very little control of the situation. "It's OK," Lorna said. "We can always call him." Yes, good point. Let's just relax everyone, it's been an odd day. It was only a short three-hour drive to Mark and Lindy's. Once we'd positioned our stuff so that we could handle any more upcoming corners and found some handles on the bench, we relaxed into the drive a bit more. I did, anyhow. Dan, I could tell, was not relaxed. Dan liked to be in control. That was when D1000 came into play. He liked to drive, to plan the route, to get everyone to the show on time. The whole idea of the Bandwagon was to give Dan a rest, let him chill out a bit rather than driving all the time. But he was not chilling out. D1000 was almost in malfunction mode, repeatedly checking on Foz through the tiny window, never getting any response, and frantically checking Google Maps on his phone. About an hour and a half into the drive, Dan lost it. "He's going the wrong fucking way! We shouldn't have come off that last exit. What the fuck is he doing?! Call him Lorna, call him now."

Lorna pulled out her phone and called Foz while Dan upped the ante on his window bashing. Nothing. Lorna said the phone was ringing out, Foz just staring forwards at the road ahead, oblivious to it all.

"Maybe we're being kidnapped," said Varley. He had a fair point. We were completely out of control of the situation, we couldn't get out of the moving vehicle, and now it was apparent we had no control over where it might be taking us. "Maybe he knows a better route?" I said, trying to be positive. Dan explained we'd taken a turn off an hour before the road we were supposed to take, and that we were currently driving into the suburbs. It didn't make much sense, that was for sure. We kept going in the wrong direction for about half an hour, not being able to do anything about it. We actually considered calling the cops. D1000 was about to explode when we suddenly hit a corner sharper than any of the corners so far. Again, Max came off the seat, while I held myself in place this time. That was followed by two more corners in quick succession before the breaks were slammed on, and the Bandwagon came screeching to a halt, people and belongings flying all over the shop in the back. Dan immediately jumped out of the van and ran to the front. My guess was to stop Foz, just in case he had a plan to start the van up again. He didn't though; he had a different plan altogether.

I climbed out of the van to find myself in the car park of a small, bleak Florida strip mall. The Bandwagon was again parked diagonally across three parking spaces. Dan had his hands in the air, holding back his frustration while a very calm Foz was chatting to him. I listened as Foz explained that he had a friend here at the mall that did tattoos, and he'd wanted to get a new tattoo for a long time, so figured that since we were passing, now might be a good time to get one.

What the fuck? Who in their right mind would think that? Especially after the whole debacle with locking the keys in the cab, making everyone late, everyone who was worse for wear and who he'd just met. Why would anyone think it would be a good idea to drive an hour in the wrong direction to get a fucking tattoo? I listened as Foz explained this to Dan, and for the first time all day, my hangover disappeared. It was so audacious, I have to admit, I was impressed. Maybe I'm going to like this guy after all, I thought. Foz calmly strode off and into the tattoo parlour next to where we were parked. Dan was left to explain the situation to everyone else. Everyone was utterly bemused. Almost like they'd given up hope, the vibe felt like the end of a long tour where everyone is over it and wants to go home and be alone, not the first day. Or, as was the case now, the day before the tour even started. There was nothing we could do but wait for him to return.

There was a supermarket in the strip mall, so I went to get some refreshments and hunt down some fruit. Which can be surprisingly tricky to find in American supermarkets. I took my sweet time about it and enjoyed the air con in the shop. On my way back to the van Foz was coming out of the tattoo parlour. He'd wasted no time. I walked over to see him. As I said, I had a newfound admiration for this crazy cat who makes wild decisions. "How'd it go, man? Did you get a one?" Foz showed me his new tattoo: a simple outline of a key on his left forearm. Seriously? "Is that to make sure you don't lock us out of the van again?" I thought this was also pretty audacious. Foz said, "Oh, no, I didn't think of that. I just like keys." Fair do's, man. Fair do's.

I can't recall the rest of the drive to Mark and Lindy's, or much of what happened when we arrived. I remember it being deep in the Florida suburbs, and the street the house was on felt like the setting of a film about UFOs and alien abductions. But then everything in America makes me think of the films I was submerged in growing up. In lieu of any rom-com activity, I found a sofa and a sleeping bag and fell into a deep, deep sleep. Which was lucky because that was the only good night's sleep I'd get for some time.

The tour started in Orlando at a venue called The Social. A short three-hour drive meant a lazy morning at Mark and Lindy's, who were terrific hosts and cooked us a cracking breakfast before we set off around noon. Dan rode in the front with Foz, just in case he had any strange urges on the drive. Knowing that he was up there made everyone else feel at ease. Hangovers now in the rearview mirror, everyone was ready to let yesterday's weirdness be swept under the rug, and get cracking with the tour we'd all been looking forward to so much. Tickets for this evening's show we're looking good, even though it was Tuesday in a town none of us had played before. My guess was a lot of Shipmates from the cruise would be in attendance. Those that had travelled long distances for the festival would generally be up for hanging around and getting another show in on their way back home, and I turned out to be right.

Tickets for the rest of the tour were up and down. Some shows had sold out nicely in advance, and some were struggling a bit. This happens on tours from time to time. Skinny were headlining, and they had by far the most significant profile out of the three of us in America. They'd played Warped Tour a bunch of times, a high profile pop-punk tour that takes music and madness to parts of America most tours miss out. Over the course of the enormous schedule, you play to thousands and thousands of people, in turn building up your own fanbase. Or so you'd hope. They'd also done a bunch of great support tours out here, most notably the Frank Turner tour the year prior: that was a fucking brilliant tour. As I mentioned, it was long, and we covered a lot of ground; the venues were big, and the audiences were amazing. Every night. Frank Turner's fanbase is something very special indeed, dedicated and passionate. And within that community, if you had Frank's stamp of approval, it went a long way. This tour had that stamp of approval. At the time, all three acts were signed to the brilliant

Xtra Mile Recordings, the same label that Frank started on and run by his manager Charlie. All three acts had played with Frank many times in the past, I mentioned in my last book about our history, so there's no need to get stuck into that again, but he was a big Skinny fan, and by all accounts, Varley's music had the same effect on Frank as it had on me.

Anyway, tonight's tickets looked good, and when tickets look good, generally so does the hospitality. The Social had an adjoining restaurant, and a table was booked for all bands and crew after soundcheck. We all sat around a huge table and were told we had free reign of the menu. The food looked fantastic. This felt like the start of the tour now. Spirits were high. Everyone was buzzing. Seeing how we'd all slept the night before and driven during the day, Foz was able to join us for dinner. My guess was that after a good feed, he'd head back to the Bandwagon and get some shut-eye. We were leaving the venue at 1am for Atlanta. A six-hour drive through the night. I sat next to Foz for dinner, keen to get to know more about the man.

The waiter went around the table, taking everyone's orders and, not a band to turn down free food, Skinny ordered enough to feed a small army. When it got to Foz though, he smiled at the waiter and said, "I'll just have a beer, please." I quickly jumped in. "The food is free, Foz, you can just order what you want. He replied, "Oh, that's OK, I don't really eat."

What the fuck does that mean? How can someone not really eat?! That's one of mankind's primal laws. If you don't eat, you die. End of story. I didn't actually say this, but clearly, everyone was thinking it, as a weird silence fell over the table that had been full of life seconds before. The waiter returned with a can of beer, which Foz opened instantly and then raised up to a table full of confused people without drinks in our hands, and said, "Cheers!" before taking a massive gulp.

Don't get me wrong. I love a beer. I fully intended to get pissed that night myself. Skinny also love a drink. As I mentioned, they pass around a Sacred Flagon of booze at their live shows, encouraging the audience to drink. We're both seen as boozy bands. That's why we work so well together. I started drinking when I was about 14 years old, and now 26 years later, I'm still as thirsty as ever. There are not many situations that a beer isn't going to improve. But there are a few exceptions: the cinema, for example, I don't like drinking if I'm going to go to the cinema, because I'll just need a piss and be that annoying guy that keeps getting up. And also driving. Drink-driving is disgusting. It's selfish, dangerous and outright fucking stupid. It's also easy to avoid, I've never done it, and I spend my life drinking and travelling. Fuck drink-driving, and anyone who thinks it's OK. It's not.

But there we were, watching our 'driver' chug down an ice-cold PBR from the tour rider. No one was really sure how to act. I think the reality was we knew that without Foz, the tour could not happen. We simply would not be able to get from gig to gig. Trying to somehow justify it to myself and playing devil's advocate in my head, I tried to make it OK. It was 5pm. We weren't leaving until 1am. Foz was just having a beer, then he'd get some kip and sleep it off, and maybe he'd feel hungry when we woke up, get some food in his belly and be fit and able to drive us to Atlanta while we all slept soundly in the back. This is what I was telling myself, but at the same time, alarm bells were ringing. I looked to Lorna, as did everyone else. Because Lorna was in charge.

Lorna is a force of nature. On stage with Skinny, she oozes charisma, singing her heart out, dancing her socks off and whipping the audience up into a frenzy. She crowd-surfs, she lets loose, and she looks the audience in the eye while she's doing it. An absolute natural. She's also a born leader, confident, intelligent and not afraid of taking the bull by the horns. Behind the scenes, she's very much captain of the good ship Skinny Lister, hence everyone looking at her in this time of need. But let's be clear, this was in no way Lorna's fault. She worked with what was on offer and had no way of knowing that our 'driver' was actually a drunk punk who didn't eat food. However much I pretended to be in the band though, truth be told, I wasn't. Lorna wasn't there to look after me. I alone am accountable for my actions and felt that I needed to do my bit in this awkward situation. So after our awkward dinner, I asked Foz if we could go outside and "have a word".

The first thing Foz said once we were alone, outside the venue in the shadow of the Bandwagon, was, "I'm really looking forward to your show tonight." Which was a great opening gambit to what I wanted to say. I explained in the politest, sternest manner that I could muster that Foz wouldn't be able to see the show tonight, or for that matter, any other night. Maybe he was unsure of what he'd signed up for, but his job was to drive the Bandwagon through the night, and because of this, he'd need to sleep in the evening. He'd also have to refrain from drinking and understand that he was undertaking a huge responsibility, not just to get us to the show on time, but also to keep us all alive. I explained that everyone was getting concerned about his erratic behaviour, what with the tattoo and not eating dinner. The best thing he could do right now is jump into the driver's bunk, which was in the van's front cab, and get some rest. We'll see you after the gig around midnight. All the while I was saying this, Foz was listening intently, and I'll be honest, I thought it was getting through. Maybe it was just a misunderstanding, and he wasn't clear what the job entailed. Maybe now we'd had this chat, everything would be back on track. Once I'd wrapped up, Foz smiled and replied, "I don't really sleep."

What the fuck?! I kind of lost it a little. "Yes, you do, Foz, you do on this tour. Get in the bunk and get some fucking sleep, or your role on the tour will be over before it's begun." I turned and walked back into the venue, unsure about how to play this or what to do now. It doesn't take a genius to work out that a lorry-driving punk who doesn't sleep and doesn't eat is a speed-head. But without this speedhead, we couldn't do the tour. Shit.

I drank myself into a stupor while Will and Skinny seemed to do the same. The gig was fantastic, and while you're in the midst of a storming show, the storm outside has a tendency to vanish. I just didn't think about it, not until the Bandwagon kicked into gear and we took off on the highway. I'd not seen Foz since he told me he doesn't sleep. I'd managed to avoid him while getting on the bus. I'd told the others about our little chat. Lorna had promised to check his sobriety before she let him drive anywhere. Apparently, the PBR dinner had been his only beer and he'd been resting while we played. And with that, we were off. I'd like to say that it put my mind at rest, but that night I lay in my coffin shaking and bumping around, waiting impatiently for death to come.

Somehow we made it to Atlanta in one piece. We arrived at The Masquerade the next morning. Only once the Bandwagon was parked did I manage to get some sleep, not waking up until mid-afternoon. The Masquerade is a beautiful venue. These days, it has a new home on the other side of town, but back then, the venue was an old mill, with three gig rooms and loads of random mill equipment kicking around. It had a great legacy, and it was a wonderful place to play. Both the other rooms also had gigs on that night, and when I stepped out of the Bandwagon that afternoon, blurry-eyed and groggy, I was greeted by the sight of two tour buses. Nothing overly fancy, but tour buses nonetheless. I'm generally not one to get jealous. I know it doesn't do anyone any favours, and I'm happy with my lot, but I have to say, looking up at those other buses made me feel envious. Not even because they looked like rock stars or anything like that. They just looked safe. Safe and capable of providing a decent night's sleep. I went into the venue and cracked open a beer for breakfast. It was 5pm, after all.

We also made it to Nashville in one piece the following day. Early in fact. I'd managed to sleep on the way too. The show in Atlanta was incredible, good enough for me to push the Foz situation even further into the back of my mind and somehow to get some sleep in transit. I woke up in Nashville at around 10am in the venue's carpark. That evening's show was to be held at a Nashville spot called The Basement. Neither Will nor I were needed until about 5pm, so we had the whole day to explore the city.

I wrote a song about my previous visit to Nashville, called 'Fuck You, Nashville'. Obviously, the song was tongue in cheek, but it's safe to say my last experience wasn't the greatest. Growing up on country music and American culture in general, Nashville held a very special place in my heart from afar. Maybe it was the huge expectations that I held for it that made it difficult to live up to. Who knows what went wrong that last visit, and to be honest, who cares? Because Nashville is fucking amazing. Will and I had an epic day. Drinking on the strip, watching songwriters play for tips, checking out guitar shops and record shops and meeting some lovely and interesting folk. We even recorded some songs direct to vinyl in a tiny little booth at Jack White's Third Man Records. It was a brilliant day. By the time showtime came around, I was wearing an 'I Love Nashville' T-shirt, Will was wearing a cowboy hat, and I just went ahead and opened up with the song 'Fuck You, Nashville'. Luckily the crowd got it and sang along, rather than not getting it and shooting me, which is what Will tried to convince me was going to happen.

The excitement of the day and another great gig came crashing down when I came off stage and went back to the Bandwagon to put away my guitar. As I opened the door to the back compartment,

I found Foz with a bottle of Jamesons, midway through a giant slug. It actually looked like he was attempting to down the thing. On seeing me, Foz tried to hide the bottle. I honestly had no idea what to say. There was no point trying to reason with Foz, so I didn't say a word; I just took the bottle, then cleared out the van of all the other booze that was hanging around. And went back to the venue, shouting "GET SOME SLEEP!" as I left.

Back in the venue, Skinny were blowing the roof clean off of The Basement. Man, they know how to throw a party. The place was jumping. But I struggled to enjoy the show, knowing that I'd have to be the bearer of bad news pretty much as soon as they came off stage. Which I was. We had an emergency tour meeting. It turned out I'd not been the only one catching Foz on the bottle; Max had seen him sneaking out a few beers, and Will had caught him in the dressing room. From what I could gather, nobody had actually seen him sleep or eat once in the last three days. Maybe he was telling the truth when he said he doesn't sleep or eat. All anyone had actually seen him do was drive and drink.

Lorna looked into other drivers (too expensive), other modes of transport (there weren't any), and other general ideas. The most positive one was trying to get Dan some kind of insurance on the Bandwagon. He didn't have the full lorry driver license needed, but apparently, with the correct insurance, he might be able to take the wheel, which all of us would have loved, Dan included, even though he'd never driven anything that size. He was 100% safer than Foz. Nothing could be done about that until the morning, when the world woke up. We had a six-hour drive to Pittsburgh. We settled on not leaving until the following morning. We could all sleep in the carpark of The Basement and make sure Foz slept too, and do the drive in the cold hard light of the next day. A bad situation, yes, but with a new added bonus of a night out in Nashville - and I'm not sure if I mentioned yet, but Nashville is fucking amazing.

We left for Pittsburgh at 10am. Dan had kept guard over Foz that night, making sure he didn't drink anymore and got some sleep, and Dan then sat up front with him while he drove, and we stressed out in the back. Will called it first. "This is the last time I ride with Foz. I don't want to die just so I can do a gig in New York. I don't care how well the tickets have sold." It's weird, because the reality of what was happening was our shared attitude towards gigging - whatever happens, the show goes ahead - was now putting our lives in danger. It was stupid, but as there was no other way to get from gig to gig, we had all tried to sweep it under the carpet. But, as usual, with those things left under the carpet, it had got worse and, of course, had to be dealt with eventually. At this point, we all agreed that unless we found a different mode of transport, we would have to pull the tour.

The six-hour drive had turned into a ten-hour drive, and we arrived in Pittsburgh late as fuck. Not a problem for Will or myself, as we come from the school of plug and play, and soundchecks are not entirely necessary. Skinny, on the other hand, with all the bells and whistles, need a soundcheck. But that wasn't going to happen tonight. We loaded in as doors opened to the sold-out show and they mic'd up the gear, knowing they'd just have to hope for the best later on.

There was something in the air that night in Pittsburgh. It felt on edge. It was a Saturday night, and the streets were heaving. Maybe it was a full moon, maybe the city was always like this. I'd not been before or since, but yeah, there was something in the air. I don't say that as a bad thing - quite the opposite. I love being a stranger in a big city on a Saturday night almost as much as I love a full moon. I was well up for it.

During the load-in to The Club Cafe, that evening's venue, Foz came up to me and said, "Do you wanna get some blow?" I actually couldn't believe it. What planet was the guy on? He seemed to be completely unaware how much he'd fucked up, how he was about to be fired any minute and how he'd pretty much screwed the tour. I couldn't even be bothered to get into it with him. I just shook my head and walked away. I had a great gig. The Saturday night crowd was also up for it, it seemed. Loud, drunk and joyous. The buzz that I'd felt on the streets of Pittsburgh was alive inside the venue, and the room was heaving.

After my show, as usual, I went straight out to the merch stand to sell my wares. On my way, I caught a glimpse of Foz. It didn't look like he'd found any blow, or if it did, he reacted to cocaine in the opposite way to me. It did look like Lorna had broken the news to him though, and more to the point he looked like a man who'd just downed a bottle of Jamesons to himself - flopping and falling all over the shop in an incoherent mess. I dodged past unnoticed, and got out to the merch stand.

Obviously, the best part of playing a gig is the time on stage. That goes without saying; that is, after all, why you do the travelling, the grafting and whatnot - all for that magic moment on the stage. I live for it. But I also love all the other aspects of playing a show, and I especially like hanging out at the merch. It's a necessary component for me, as merch sales are my bread and butter, and even if someone else is on hand to sell, you always sell a shit-load more if you take the time to do it yourself. But that's not why I love it. It's the meeting people, that's what I love. I'm not aware of any other job where you get to travel around the world, and everywhere you go, you have people who are automatically your friend. As far as I'm aware, that only happens in the arts. It's a beautiful thing.

I could probably write a whole chapter about merch, about selling T-shirts, CDs and books. About venue commission, sales techniques or the position of the merch table. Now's not the time for that, but on this fateful night, the merch table was right in the thick of it - as you'd imagine, my favourite spot. The Club Cafe in Pittsburgh wasn't the biggest of venues, and the merch stand was kind of squeezed in on the edge of the dancefloor. As mentioned, the place was rammed, over-capacity I'd say. Hanging-from-the-rafters kind of vibe. A merch stand like this is excellent because you also get to watch the show. Sometimes, you can be plonked in a bar or a separate room from where the stage is. Not tonight though, and with the gig running late, change over was minimal. So I ran straight down and got started shifting as much as possible before Skinny kicked off and rightly stole the attention away.

The first people in the queue actually held my attention for most of the changeover, meaning sales were shit, but the banter was top notch. I'd describe the two guys as Hillbilly Jocks, and I don't mean that in a condescending way. They were a right laugh. Both huge, built like brick shit-houses, loud as fuck, over-confident and completely hammered. I'm not sure if they even bought a T-shirt. I think they just swapped one for a round of shots and a heavy-handed pat on the back. You could tell they had a big night planned, and in my mind, I kind of presumed my night might be heading the same direction. As Skinny kicked off, I was given two enormous bear hugs. After telling me how much they loved me, the two of them disappeared into the throng of people.

The next time I saw them was ten minutes later. Some kind of kerfuffle caused the crowd to part, and through the opening in the throng, I saw Foz punching one of the Hillbilly Jocks in the face. It was a pathetic punch, thrown by a drunk and pathetic man. It was like water off a duck's back to my new found friend, who had clearly seen his fair share of fistfights. He launched himself at Foz, grabbed him by the scruff of the neck and raised his fist, about to perform a punch that would be anything but pathetic. His friend, also a fucking hard nut, kind of looked around the crowd for someone else to launch themselves into. The whole thing was about to erupt into a bar brawl, and nobody knew why.

Skinny, as I have mentioned, can work a crowd into a frenzy. Obviously, it's not fighting music, far from it, but when a crowd is charged, I guess there's always the capacity for a fuse to be lit. Especially if some idiot in the crowd starts hitting people for no reason, looking for trouble. I saw how the whole thing that was about to unfold: Hillbilly Jock hits Foz, it looks like he started it, someone intervenes, other Hillbilly Jock hits them, chaos endures, and the gig is ruined. Obviously, I couldn't let that happen.

I've worked in enough pubs to have seen a few fights in my time. I've never personally had a fight. I'm a pacifist. The most interaction with fights I've had is stopping them, or at least trying to. This comes with the territory of working at a pub in London. I've always found that stopping a fight is easier than you'd think. Deep down, no one really wants to fight. Show them a way out, and they'll generally take it. So without thinking, I stormed through the crowd and showed the two Hillbilly Jocks the way out.

I'm still not sure how exactly it worked. I just kind of opened my arms wide, ran over to the two huge guys, and shimmied them towards the exit. Before I knew it, I was outside the venue with both the Jocks, who were fucking pissed off. Not at me though; they still loved me.

"THAT FUCKING DUDE CLOCKED ME IN THE FACE"

"I'M GONNA KILL HIM"

"BEANS - WE'RE GONNA KILL HIM"

I heard Skinny kick back into the next song from the venue behind me, and I realised the gig was saved - so far, at least. I was hoping someone had the sense to deal with Foz, to stop him from hitting anyone else. I knew for sure that he'd thrown the first punch here and was planning to go down in flames since his recent firing. I knew I had to keep my new-found friends from killing him, even if he'd brought the whole thing on himself - for the sake of the gig more than the safety of the guy who'd been trying to kill me for the past week.

"Listen, guys, he's with the band, he's a prick, he'll be dealt with, but no way can you go back in and ruin the gig for Skinny."

"BEANS, WE LOVE YOU, MAN. BUT WE'RE STILL GONNA KILL HIM"

I was very glad that I was still loved in this situation. I like to think that I would have reacted just as quickly and effectively if the same thing had gone down without me having already met the Jocks, but who knows? I might just have gotten a broken nose. Either way, I knew I was safe. I just needed to keep the situation from exploding again.

"Guys, let's get a drink!" I said joyously

"Shots. My shout." And without waiting for a response, I walked off, not looking back until the venue was out of sight and mind. Ahead I spotted a neon bar sign, and either side of me were my two new pals.

"WE LOVE YOU BEANS" they said in unison.

Two minutes later,we were sat at the bar in a joint called The Smiling Moose. All three of us smiling, drinking shots, as they were telling me about the life of a Pennsylvanian hard nut. The gig had been saved, and in my head, I imagined myself as some kind of hero. For my heroic acts, I'd have to forfeit my post-gig shift on the merch stand, missing out on some much-needed dollar, but I guess that's the price you pay.

One of the guys' phone rang, and he excitedly explained to whoever was calling (and the rest of the bar) that he was drinking with "Beans on fucking Toast!" And "doing shots!" Man, this guy was loud. "Yeah, at The Smiling Moose. Come on over!" he said and then looked at his pal and said, "They're all on their way!"

"All", it turned out, was the whole family. They'd all driven into town together to watch the show. The whole family were Beans on Toast fans. They all "fucking loved" me (their words). Loved me enough, it seemed, to forgo the rest of the Skinny Lister gig in order to come and drink at a different bar, just because I was there. More new friends. The more, the merrier.

Or at least that's what I thought. Five family members turned up. I'm not sure who was related to who, or how, and I never did find out. They were all as big as my new mates, if not bigger and just as hammered. But these Moose were not smiling. They were still annoyed about what had happened at the venue.

"Man, you should have killed that guy!" I tried to lay on the charm to the new arrivals and get them into the good time spirit we had going, but it didn't have the desired effect, so I got a big round of shots in. This also didn't have the desired effect. They brought the fighty, aggy energy that Foz had created in the venue into this bar with them. Just as the shots went down, a stranger bumped into one of the family members, and they erupted. Screaming, shouting, swearing, pushing and shoving. No actual violence but mass aggro flying around in all directions and threats of violence falling like rain on the Ohio River. I considered my options and bolted.

I've never had a problem with an Irish exit. My best mate Dave Danger is the fucking king of them, and he's the nicest person I know, so no way can they be rude. There was every possibility that a fight was about to happen, but this one had sweet fuck all to do with me. I'd had my fill of violent outbursts for the night (if not the year), so while no one was looking, I got the fuck out of Dodge and headed back to Club Cafe to receive my hero's welcome.

I'm not the hero of this story. As I mentioned earlier, that crown goes to D1000. But there was another hero in the midst that night.

Scott. As I got back to the venue, the show had finished, and the club was being cleared and reset for a club night (known as a Disco loadout). The merch table was long gone, so I wormed my way back to the dressing room. The mood in there was strangely sober. Sober, but not sombre. The smell of good news was in the air. Foz was gone, thank fuck, and in my absence, a plan had been formulated.

I'd met Scott many times, at Frank Turner or Flogging Molly shows, a lovely gentleman who loved music, loved touring musicians and happened to be stinking rich. He'd become a kind of Folk Punk Philanthropist, helping out many bands from sticky situations. He once bought me a plane ticket from Texas to New Orleans to support Flogging Molly. They'd offered me a show, but there wasn't enough money to cover travel, and he'd stepped in to save the day. He loved Skinny Lister and was good friends with the whole band. He'd apparently caught wind of what was going on and, taking one look at Foz, stepped in to sort the situation out with the all-powerful, problem-solving attributes of a kind heart and a big wallet.

In short, he offered to pay for a professional, sober and capable driver to drive the Bandwagon for the rest of the tour, and had helped in the arranging of sorting that someone out. That person could start the following day in Cleveland. Some kind of one-day emergency insurance cover had been obtained, which meant that Dan would be able to drive the Bandwagon the three-hour drive the following day. Hotels had been laid on for the night, too. Hence the sober mood, everyone was packing up their shit and heading to a hotel room with a hot shower and a bed, that wasn't in the back of a van being driven by a lunatic. We all thanked Scott profusely and went to load the shit back into the Bandwagon.

During loadout, two things happened. Firstly, Foz reappeared. He'd lost a front tooth. Nobody had seen him since he threw the punch in the pit. Everyone had kind of presumed it had been me that had got him out of the venue, but apart from that, nobody really cared. Happy to see the back of him. But here he was, looking in a worse state than ever before. I guess he'd found some coke, as it was all over his face. My presumption was that he'd spent the money Lorna had given him to get home (wherever that might be) when she told him it was game over and he would no longer be on the tour.

Foz looked at me through his drug-addled eyes, and I could still see a fondness there. He still had strange calmness about him. I could tell that, even now, he had no idea that he'd fucked up. Even after being sacked, he still thought it was all part of it. Like he couldn't read emotions from anyone else or paid no attention to the situation around him, even as it went from bad to worse.

"Maybe we could get tour tattoos?" he said to me, lifting up his sleeve to expose the tattoo of the key he'd got way back in Florida.

"Maybe we will, Foz, maybe we will."

And with that, he turned and vanished into the bustling Pittsburgh Saturday night.

The next thing that happened was just fucking weird. About two minutes after Foz's bizarrely emotional departure, another fight kicked off, right outside the venue, while we were loading out. But this fight was like a scene from a Hollywood movie. It started as a guy ran past, full pelt, like he was being chased. He tripped up on the bass amp in the middle of the sidewalk (pavement), which was waiting to be put in the van. He hit the floor and scuttled into the doorway of a closed cigar shop that was next to the venue, looking freaked-out as fuck. The next minute a dude runs by, spots him, and grabs him by the scruff of the neck. The dude looks like Bruce Willis, or some kind of hardcore action hero, the chap he's picking up off the floor looks like a nerdy computer programer. The whole situation happens as if we're not there, as if there weren't five English musicians crowding round a weird-looking tour bus van, watching someone about to receive the kicking of a lifetime.

"WHERE IS THE KEY?" the action man shouted at the nerdy computer guy.

"I promise I don't have the key… Please. I don't have it," he pleaded back.

"EVERYTHING IS ABOUT THE KEY. GIVE ME THE KEY, AND I'LL LET YOU GO!" He looked like he was going to kill him when, without any thought or even knowing why or what I was doing, I blurted out:

"The key went that way!" and pointed off into the direction Foz, and his key tattoo, had gone.

My English accent destroyed the feature film feeling of the whole event. Skinny all turned to me like I was a mad-man. Why the fuck was I getting involved in this serious-as fuck situation that has nothing to do with me?

I pointed again and repeated myself: "The Key went that way, mate."

The action man dropped the nerdy guy and ran in the direction that I'd pointed, the nerdy guy ran in the other direction, and the movie finished. Everyone looked at me like, what the fuck?!

I guess I was desperate to take the hero moniker back from Scott. Who knows? We didn't have time to ponder it. We still had to finish loadout, which we did, then people headed to the bonus hotel Scott had provided. I headed back to The Smiling Moose for a night I'd soon forget.

The following morning, bright-eyed and bushy-tailed Dan: singer, songwriter and frontman of the fabulous Skinny Lister, switched a switch and became D1000. He then drove us all, the whole touring family, safely and happily to Cleveland. It was the nicest drive of the whole tour. Dan had never driven anything of this size before, but we trusted him with all our hearts, and we all knew we'd narrowly escaped some kind of horrific drink driving incident in the hands of a hooligan. The tour was saved. The show would go on. On arrival at The Grog shop in Cleveland, the venue had left some cones out to keep a parking spot for us on a busy street. The gap was the exact same size as the Bandwagon, with two vehicles on either side. It was going to be impossible to get the van in there, no matter how good at reverse parking you might be. Impossible - but not for D1000. Without missing a beat, Dan reversed parked this mahoosive beast of a vehicle in one beautiful movement. It was glorious. Like a dance. Like a kiss. Like a sunset.

Roll credits....

That's the end of this story, but it certainly wasn't the end of the tour. That night in Cleveland at The Grog shop, a live chicken appeared out of thin air while I was playing on stage. But that, my friends, is a story for another time.

THE BLAG

"I'm here from Viper Magazine to interview the band." I'd used this blag many times before, so far with a 100% success rate. But never in a venue of this size. It was 5pm, I know that for sure, probably a weekday and sometime in the year 2000. I was at the entrance to Dingwalls, a 500-capacity music venue just off Camden Lock.

I know it was 5pm because I actually used to refer to this as the '5pm blag'. I normally used it in bigger venues, like The Astoria, a 2,000 capacity venue in the West End. That was where this blag was invented, to see a band called Everclear, I think. I had little-to-no money but lots of ideas, a general understanding of how music venues worked, and the kind of confidence you hold when you have nothing to lose.

I didn't work for Viper Magazine. The magazine didn't exist. But the lone guy on the door didn't know that, or if he did know, then he didn't care. The same old dude always sat on the door at The Astoria, checking who was going in and out before the security and show promoters turned up around six-ish. He just nodded me through. Pen and paper in my hand, I smiled and walked on by. Once inside the venue, I went straight to the toilet, locked myself in a cubicle and waited for two hours until doors opened and people started using them. That was my cue to walk out and enjoy the gig. The gig was fucking brilliant too. Worth every penny.

I pulled that blag loads of times at The Astoria and a few times at other venues around the same size. Always at 5pm, always from Viper Magazine, and always nodded in without question. I soon stopped locking myself in the toilet when it became abundantly clear that if you looked like you were supposed to be there, nobody gave a shit, and nobody would question you. I'd just sit watching bands I loved soundcheck, and if anyone looked my way, I'd just smile and nod. Then the doors would open.

Dingwalls was smaller though, and there was a big difference: I had everything to lose. Grandaddy. My favourite band were playing that night. It was sold out. Not that I had any money, even if it wasn't. I needed to see the show, I needed it with every ounce of my being, so the 5pm blag was my only option. However, without my 'nothing to lose' confidence, I instantly screwed up the blag.

"I'm here from Viper Magazine to interview the band."

I answered someone who hadn't even asked me a question as I stepped in the door. I should have just fucking walked in, but I choked. The dude who clearly didn't work at the venue looked confused and tried to be helpful.

"Oh, OK. Let's see… SARAH!", he shouted out just as a short, serious-looking brown-haired woman walked around the corner. Mateyboy points at me, I look nervous and awkward, and he says, "Someone to interview the band," and steps out the door.

"Hello, I'm Sarah, the press officer for Grandaddy. What time is the interview scheduled for?"

"5pm," is all I can muster.

"What magazine?"

"Viper."

Every other time I'd said "Viper Magazine", it had sounded legit, I fucking believed it, and I'd made it up. This time, however, saying it out loud sounded like utter nonsense. So I tried to reinforce it.

"It's a student magazine from a university."

"Oh, from a university? That's a great place for a student magazine," she said sarcastically as she pulled out a clipboard. "Interviews aren't supposed to start until 6pm today." She's got a fucking schedule! Nothing like this has ever happened before. I'm about to turn around and leg it when the mood flips completely. She looks up, smiles and says, "You know what, the guys are waiting to start the soundcheck. It's taking forever, so let's just do it now. Follow me."

I follow.

We walk through an empty venue, OK, sort of empty. Bar staff are setting up the bar. There's a Sparklehorse song being played really loudly and a stressed-out looking dude behind the sound desk, frantically twisting dials that make the song dart from one speaker to the next. The stage itself looks like beautiful chaos. I'd never seen Grandaddy, my favourite band, play live before. I had no idea what to expect, but the stage looked bang on. Beat up guitars all over the shop, keyboards that looked like they'd been raised from the dead by the god of gaffa tape, and shrubbery. It looked like they'd spent the afternoon on Hampstead Heath pulling out branches and collecting twigs and leaves. The whole thing was joined by leads tangled up in a beautiful mess, and as you would imagine, right in the middle of it all, looking even more stressed than the guy behind the desk, was another soundman, on stage trying to make sense of it all, gaffa tape in hand.

This incredible sight had my full attention until I realised precisely what was happening. I was being taken to the dressing room to interview Grandaddy. My favourite band. For an imaginary magazine. They say never meet your heroes. I'm not sure if that's true. I'd say it's more along the lines of, be careful where you meet your heroes. Or how.

At this point in my life, I'd only been in a few dressing rooms. But it only takes a few to realise they are more functional than rock'n'roll history books would lead you to believe. I'm sure it's different if you're Guns N' Roses. But Grandaddy were not, and so I followed Sarah into a cramped room with a sour mood hanging in the air and no windows. Sarah cut through the tension with "This is..." She trailed off as she looked at me and realises she didn't know my name. "Jay," I said, as she glanced at her schedule, realising I wasn't on there either. "Yes, Jay from...." The same thing happened. "Viper Magazine."

"Yes, of course, a student magazine all the way from a university." Sarah looked at me, the mood flipped back to serious, and she said, "You've got 15 minutes," then walked out the door.

Truth is: I'm an awful liar. I hate lies. They ruin the world they run. It is, however, a very fine line between a lie and a blag. I'm confident I know where that line is, or where I think it is anyway. For example, saying you're from a magazine to get into a venue, that's a blag. Fine. Actually, sitting down with someone for 15 minutes, keeping up the pretence that you work for a magazine, that's a lie. But what the fuck else am I supposed to do?

I pull the pen and notepad out and say quietly, "Do you mind if I ask you some questions?"

The mood of the room warms. Whatever it was that was stressing everyone out is put on the back burner, I'm offered a drink, and after a bit of a rearranging kerfuffle, I'm sat on the sofa surrounded by the band. I have their full attention as they all sit waiting for me to say something.

Now I could talk about Grandaddy's music until the cows came home. I knew the lyrics to the album *Under the Western Freeway* like they were etched into my soul, but I knew very little about them. I'd seen a few photos and read one thing in a magazine about them. They were from California. But not from

LA or San Francisco, from a town in California I'd never heard of. The music was otherworldly, and so were the band. Five dudes that looked like skateboarders in farmers outfits with enormous beards. Their music was futuristic and intensely connected to nature, like a computer, alone in a desert during a beautiful sunset. So I just said:

"I really love your music."

They smiled, nodded politely and waited for me to actually start the interview. I had no idea how interviews were supposed to go. I mean, obviously, I could guess, but it's not like I had any dreams of being a music journalist or read that much music press. What sort of questions are you supposed to ask?

"Tell me about the new album."

Boom. They were off, my favourite band sat in a tiny room, telling me in full enthusiastic detail about the very album I'd been counting down the days to hear.... And I didn't hear a word of it. Surrounded by this lie I'd created, I wasn't even star-struck or thinking about how I was sitting there with my favourite band. I was thinking about how all this was going to play out, and wondering how I would keep it up for 13 more minutes, all the while pretending to make notes about what they were saying. I felt like I was in a nightmare. Then it hit me. Tell the truth. Honesty is the best policy. Fuck, they're going to love it. I'll tell them all about the 5pm blag, being skint, loving the band. Maybe we can just hang out as buddies all night, friends forever!

"I'm not actually from Viper magazine."

I kind of blurted it out, stopping Jason Lytle, the singer and my hero, in his tracks. He was mid-flow, explaining the hopes and dreams he had for this incredible body of work that he'd created, but I talked over him, so he stopped.

"What do you mean?" chimed in Jim, the guitarist, who hadn't said a word yet.

I let it roll out. Telling the truth felt fantastic. I told the story about The Astoria and blagging it into gigs and locking myself in the toilets, the whole shebang.

"Why don't you just buy a ticket like everyone else who's coming to the gig tonight?" said Jim. He wasn't impressed with my super blag; more annoyed, I'd say.

"I'm skint," I explained.

"Doesn't seem fair to me," Jim said, and the rest of the band nodded in agreement. "Everyone else had to pay."

Fuck, yes, of course. I mean, he's got a point. "It's just a blag. I wanted to see the show," I said. "I'll just go, sorry!" I think my plan was to head straight to the toilet, back to plan A.

"No, hold up." Jason talked for the first time since I so rudely interrupted his monologue.

"There's got to be a way you can see the show. Maybe you can do something to earn it?" The band also agreed this could work.

"I have an idea," Jason said, and he stood up and grabbed a huge pile of posters for *The Sophtware Slump* from the table. "These fucking posters have the wrong release date for the album in the corner. If you take these posters, rip all the corners off all the posters and put all the posters up, you can stay and watch the gig."

Mr Jayson Lytle, you have a deal.

I'm not sure if Jason underestimated the number of posters in the pile or my sheer enthusiasm, but by the time doors opened, the venue was plastered with posters. Every wall, every door, every cubicle. Even a few posters were up on the ceiling. The merch stand looked like some kind of *Sophtware Slump* shrine, exploding with posters. Each poster had the bottom right corner ripped off, which was kind of cool because that was the vibe of the band too, tatty. Grandaddy soundchecked my two favourite songs while I worked, and I'd blagged a beer from the soundman. Now it's on!

If I'm honest, I remember the events before the gig better than the gig itself. And that's not to disrespect the gig in any way, which was out of this world. It's fucking weird thinking back to it now, watching a band you loved but knew absolutely nothing about except for the songs. It feels so alien now. These days, the minute you hear a song you like, you can see all the music they've released, photos, bios, content, content, content. When I fell in love with Grandaddy, I just had one CD. All that mattered was the music. It was great. Anyways, we're not here to talk about music. We're here to talk about blags.

Around the time of that Grandaddy gig, I'd started a job flyering for a bunch of indie nights in Camden and the West End. I talk about this in my last book. I loved the job and blagged into countless gigs off the back of being the flyer guy. As I started getting more involved with putting on gigs and club nights, I began to get pretty good at getting myself on the guestlist for gigs. A very easy blag, but a good one. I've been to lots and lots of gigs in my time. Big gigs, small gigs, country gigs, heavy metals gigs, gigs in laundrettes, gigs on pig farms, life-changing gigs, boring-as-fuck gigs, busy gigs, empty gigs... If there's a bunch of people on a stage in a dark room making a racket, I'm basically up for it. And thinking back now, I can count the tickets that I've bought for shows on one hand. There's always been a blag. As someone who now pretty much makes a living from people buying tickets to my shows, this is either tremendous or tragic. Maybe a bit of both; personally I've never been afraid of a contradiction.

After a few solid years of flyering, I was promoted by two chaps that I used to flyer for. The company was called Automatic Promotions, and Geoff and Roger, who ran it, took me under their wing. I got a job in the office there, helping to run the club nights and organise other people flyering. The office was based in the legendary and now-defunct Fortress Studios in Old Street. It was a multi-floored building that housed a few incredible studios, a bunch of production suites and some creative offices. They had an in-house bar full of fascinating folk, and a couple of sneaky sidelines that probably kept the whole thing afloat. Incredible music was made in the building too. The Future Sound of London had a studio upstairs, Jacknife Lee had a studio next door, and the band Elbow had a rehearsal space. They'd lock up the studios at the weekend and open up the basement and throw lawless parties. From hard house techno raves to industry shindigs and surprise Libertines gigs. It was an exciting place to be and a sweet job to land for 20-year-old me.

While working for Automatic Promotions, we were offered a bunch of tickets to Roskilde Festival in Copenhagen to give away as a prize at one of our club nights in exchange for promoting the festival to a London audience. Would you believe it? I won a pair of tickets. It was 2001, and the festival was being headlined by Neil Young and Bob Dylan - an opportunity that I, of course, could not miss. The only problem was I had no way of getting myself and Clare, my girlfriend at the time, to Copenhagen. And neither of us had enough money to buy tickets. So I blagged it. I made a short phone call to Eurolines, a couch company that ran a service from London Victoria to central Copenhagen, and convinced them to exchange a pair of coach tickets for some of their logos on our Roskilde flyers. They were up for it, and again, I ended up winning the tickets. It was too easy. This time, it actually was. When Clare and I turned up to collect our tickets, bags packed, ready and raring to go, nobody knew anything about our free coach tickets. I had no proof of the phone call where the deal had been arranged. I had to convince the lady in the ticket office the morning the coach was leaving, then had to convince the coach driver. They really didn't want to let us on the couch, and the driver then tried to make us get off at every major stop along the way, as he'd not heard a word back from the head office that my story checked out. No way we were going to get off though: it was Bob Dylan and Neil Young, playing the same fucking festival. We made it all the way and there and all the way back on the gift of the gab, and let me tell you, it was worth every penny.

Now, blags aren't always about getting into gigs or festivals for nothing. Far from it. More often than not, they're about getting free drinks, and I've seen a few drink blags in my day. My favourite was probably my mate Ashby at Secret Garden Party around 2010 - a festival both of us knew very well, and for me personally will always be one of the best parties ever. But that's no secret.

Ashby stood up from our circle of friends that had been sitting on the floor in the sunshine chatting shit, getting fucked up and having a laugh. He walked straight into the bar inside the tent we were sitting outside, but he didn't just walk into the tent. He walked straight behind the bar and started serving people waiting for drinks. Ashby is a magic man, and as usual, he was on one. He'd also worked in bars for years, be it in the local pub or at a festival. He knew what he was doing. SGP was a wonderful affair. Everyone who worked the bar was there for the same reason as the people on stage or those who had bought tickets. He fit right in. He worked the bar for 20 minutes, nobody said a word. Soon after he was part of the furniture, one of our friends then walked up to the bar, queued up and waited for Asby to ask, "What can I get you?"

"Four double rum and cokes, please."

"No problem, that's 50p."

And so it began.

One by one, we walked up to the bar and ordered the kind of drink you'd order if it was your bar. Which, of course, it wasn't. Each time the price went down. It was 12p by the time I got around to getting my double Zubrowka and Apple juice in a pint glass with loads of ice. Man, that drink tasted heavenly.

What made that a blag and not just a crime? Of course, in the legal sense, Ashby committed a crime. We all did. But in reality, it didn't feel like he did. Nobody gave a shit, nobody took too much, nobody got hurt, and nobody got caught. But more than anything, it was done in the name of jest, not in the name of greed.

Another wonderful blag that I witnessed was from someone who's name I never knew, but I've always referred to him as the 'coin man'. This is going back to my flyering days again. As well as flyering the queue of people going into gigs, I also flyered Camden Tube Station every Friday and Saturday night for whatever clubnight was happening up the road at The Barfly. There was a classic cast of characters that I would call regulars who would hang around the tube. A heady mix of buskers, beggars, scammers and nutters. My favourite was definitely an old Jamaican hot dog seller called Sam. What a legend. Although I have to say I'd never ever eat a sausage from his hideous cart, and I couldn't believe anybody in their right mind would, to be honest. And then there was the coin man.

He didn't look like a genius, he didn't act like a genius, but then I guess who does? He had long thin greasy hair pulled down in curtains going way past his shoulders, small John Lennon style circular spectacles and a short and unkempt beard. He wore a hippy-style ex-military jacket and a pair of old and ill-fitting jeans. He had a bum bag around his waist, and on his back, he had a huge rucksack. Inside this rucksack, he had ice-cold cans of Stella and packs of 20 B&H Gold cigarettes, both in abundance, and he sold them to the revellers of Camden at a bargain price and with a smile. He wouldn't be at the tube station religiously like Sam and me. He'd pop up for a weekend or two here and there, he was never pissed, and I never saw him smoke one of the many fags he sold. We'd often get chatting, in between both pimping our wares at the hordes of people streaming out of the tube station in single file looking for a good time. I'd always blag a beer and a few fags off him, which he was cool with. One of those days, in conversation, I asked him how much he made from each pack of fags he sold. As I asked, the expression on his face kind of changed, and a twinkle in his eye appeared that I'd not seen before.

"£4," he said.

"Profit?"

"Yep, £4 profit on each pack."

This was obviously nonsense because he was selling the fags at £3.50 a packet.

"Yeah, right," I said and nodded a nod that said, I'm not a fucking idiot, mate.

"I suppose if I were to be pedantic about it, the profit would actually be about £3.98. But for me personally, yeah it's £4 profit. I bet you think that sounds impossible, don't you?" He smiled as he talked to me.

"Mate, that is impossible. No doubt your making a trip over to Calais and filling your boots with Stella and B&H in a country that doesn't tax the fuck out of booze and cigarettes, then bringing it back here and making a few bob. But no, it's not possible for you to make more than you're selling them for."

"Why don't you ponder on it tonight?" he said. "I'll see you tomorrow, and if you can guess how I do it, I'll give you a pack of 20 B&H for free." And he strolled off into the tube station and disappeared down the escalators.

There wasn't anything for me to ponder, no matter how made up I'd be with a pack of 20. The dude was obviously another Camden nut job. But I have to admit I did eagerly await his return the following night and kind of jumped on him when he did finally arrive. I gave up flyering for a bit while we chatted, and he told me a little story…

When he was young, he was obsessed with coins, a manic coin collector with coins from all over the world. He still had love for the little things throughout his life, and let his collection grow alongside his hair. At some point, he started seeing similarities between certain coins, and realising that some coins worth a small amount in one country were the same size and weight as coins that were worth much more in another country. The pinnacle of this was the New Zealand to Switzerland transfer, where a Kiwi coin worth about two pence was exactly the same as a Swiss coin worth £2. He tracked down a friend of a friend of a friend who lived in Wellington, saved up some money for a flight to Switzerland, and his enterprise began.

Since then, he'd been flying out to Switzerland, putting 4p worth of coins into a cigarette machine, getting a pack of 20 fags and 50p change. Meaning every pack he sold for £3.50 he was actually making £4 profit, or if you wanted to be pedantic, £3.98.

Wow. I told you, didn't I? The man was a genius. He then explained that the Stellas just come from Tescos. You can buy them for 50p and sell them for £1, provided they're ice cold. Still a tremendous markup.

And that wasn't all. Coin man said that the best place to ransack the cigarette machines was in and around the ski resorts, so he started flying in and out of a tiny airport that fed into the Alps and provided minimal fuss from customs. He then bought himself a second-hand pair of skis. He'd worked out that all Swiss people skied on a one day pass, although most wouldn't use it all day, very much like the Tube in London at the time.

"You must have blagged a travelcard before?" he asked. Yes, of course, I had. It was pretty standard procedure back then. If you didn't need to use your one-day travelcard for the tube anymore, there would always be someone waiting at the exit keen to take it off your hands. I'd both given and been given many times. It was a good system. He explained it was the same with a ski pass in Switzerland, apart from the fact that nobody ever asked if you'd finished with your ski pass. He started waiting at the bottom of the slopes, and he said that each time, in less than 30 minutes, a confused Swiss skier would more than happily part with a card that they no longer had a use for, and so he could go skiing for free. Since then, he'd been splitting his life, half his time in Switzerland ransacking cigarette machines all morning and skiing all afternoon, and the other half in the UK, selling cheap fags and cold Stella at a few choice locations.

What a legend. I never saw coin man again after that night. No idea why, but I get the feeling he's doing alright. I raise a cold can of Stella in his honour from time to time.

Now I've never ran a life-long blag like that. Was that even a blag? Or was it another criminal enterprise? Again it's a fine line, but one that I can see quite clearly. I think that, seeing as no one was getting hurt here, and that fact it was just so fucking random, it falls onto the side of a blag. Personally, my blags have always been more about getting shit for free or having a laugh rather than trying to spin a few quid. Blagging drink or drugs, a free ride, a festival ticket, a hot meal and generally more for the fun of it than anything else. But I've also blagged making an album in one of the finest studios in the world for free and a free breakfast at the Breakfast Club.

The dictionary definition of a 'blag' is to manage to obtain something by using persuasion or guile. But to me, that sounds too sinister. It feels like they're missing all the fun out of it, and in my book (hello), it's the fun that's the important bit.

The best blag though is blagging a gig. And even if I do say so myself, that is something I've always been good at. To be honest, it's probably my gig blagging skills as much as my songwriting skills that have got me to this point where you're reading my book.

There's more than I can list, so I won't bother, but I will tell you about the best gig that I nearly blagged but didn't come off. Zoo Thousand and Eight. That was the name of the festival. I very much doubt you've heard of it because it only happened once, and it was an absolute disaster.

Situated somewhere in Kent, it was sold as a festival in a zoo, giving the impression that in between watching The Hives, Bloc Party or Dizze Rascal, you'd be able to hang out with a flamingo or a look at a lion in a cage, if that was your thing. But that wasn't the case at all. The whole thing was a farce. It was held in a field next to a zoo, to which you had no access, and seemed to be organised by someone who had no idea what a festival was. Hours of queues, no lights in the campsite, no taps and overflowing toilets from day one. They didn't have litter pickers or any bins. They also didn't have a production office, so bands would arrive, and there would be no one with any information for them. Bands also hadn't been paid advances and were not showing up. At some point, the tent housing the second stage actually fell down. It was nuts. And of course, it was raining.

I was wearing two hats that weekend, as the band I managed at the time, The Holloways, were down to play the main stage on Sunday, and I'd blagged myself a Beans show in the tent that housed the smallest stage. This was before I had an album out or anybody really wanted to see me play.

I arrived on the Friday and went to the main stage after not being able to find the production office that didn't exist. I was doing a recce for The Holloways show on Sunday. I witnessed the shit-show up close: nobody knowing stage times, bands being moved from other stages and bands not showing up. It was chaos. And nobody was in charge. So I went and got my guitar.

I then stood at the side of the stage, got my guitar out and started tuning it up. Getting ready for a gig, I stood there looking like I knew what was going on for ten minutes until the band on stage wrapped up and then I introduced myself to the person who looked the least confused.

"Where do you want me?" I said loudly over the front of house music and loadout sounds.

"Who are you?" said the man unplugging the monitor at the front of the stage. I'd walked over to him and was now front and centre of the main stage.

"I'm Beans on Toast, I'm on next."

"No, you're not mate. Funeral For A Friend are on next."

And then I dived in.

"What the hell is up with this festival? Nobody knows what's going on. I've been told 100 different things by 100 different people. And there's not even a zoo here. I'm here to play. I'm just supposed to be doing a couple of tunes during the changeover before Funeral For A Friend. John confirmed the whole thing. It's just one mic and a DI for my guitar." John, of course, didn't exist.

"Nobody's told me anything about this, but you're right. This place is insane." He smiled and plugged the monitor back in. "If John says so," he said, "then let's do it." And he started setting up what I needed to plug in and play.

Now the festival was, as I said, a shit-show. But the line up was incredible. As well as all the great bands aforementioned, also playing were The Cribs, Pendulum, Calvin Harris and Chas & Dave, to name a few. And the turnout was huge. While I was standing on the stage, convincing the guy that I was supposed to be there and supposed to be playing some songs, around 4,000 people were standing in front of the stage. The gig I was booked to play would have been more like 40. This was going to be the blag of the century.

The chap set me up and told the sound team that I was scheduled to play. Nobody questioned it. It was all rolling. I soundchecked my guitar through my stage monitor and gave the thumbs up, eagerly awaiting someone to turn off the front of house music so I could kick off the biggest show I'd ever played. Playing to way more people than I ever had before. Way more. Completely uninvited. It was going to be incredible.

But it wasn't.

"Beans on Toast!" A completely new person I'd not seen on the stage yet came bounding over.

"Yes, hi, are we good to go?" I gave my guitar a little strum to signal: I'm ready.

"What are you doing? You're supposed to be playing the little tent over there."

I was rumbled.

I kept at it.

"No, that's all changed now. This place is so disorganised. John cleared it. I'm just going to do a few tunes during the changeover. I'm ready to go. We've soundchecked and everything."

"I'm John," said John. Turns out he did exist after all.

"The stage manager."

Shit. Double rumbled.

I give it one last-ditch attempt. "Please man, just let me play. I'm all set. Just one song."

John, it turned out, was no fool. He saw right through me from the off. "Not today, mate. Nice try, now get off my stage."

And so it didn't happen. Perhaps a sliding door moment in my life. Who knows what would have happened if I could've played that gig? Would things have gone differently? Who cares?

Poor organisational skills aside, it was an incredible weekend. I blew the roof off the little tent, and the 40 people in the crowd went wild. I also made sure The Holloways were well placed. I managed to get them on main support to The Hives, who were headlining Sunday night. More bands had pulled out, and I was there to help out and bump them up to a better slot. I also managed to get their fee paid upfront of the performance. So many bands were not turning up because they hadn't been paid.

The event was a success, from where I was standing anyhow. Probably best that the world was never given a Zoo Thousand and Nine though.

Sometimes a blag is just making cool shit happen. A few years after the whole Grandaddy shenanigans, my 'favourite band' tag had moved on. It was now a San Francisco duo called Two Gallants. Me and my girlfriend at the time were completely obsessed with them. This must have been around 2006. I was living at Nambucca, the infamous music venue on the Holloway Road at the time, and me and my girlfriend would lie in bed for hours, smoking weed and listening to the Two Gallants, obsessing over the deep heart wrenching lyrical genius combined with insane drum patterns and passionate guitar and harmonica playing.

One day around that time, I left the house for some tedious chore, maybe to get some fags, and while I was minding my own business, singing a Two Gallants song under my breath, walking up the Holloway Road wearing an oversized ex-military jacket (the influence of coin man perhaps?), I looked up. And there, right in front of me, were Adam and Tyson - the Two Gallants. Adam was also wearing an oversized combat jacket. I couldn't fucking believe it. Having met a darn sight more musicians and folk that I admire since the whole Grandaddy showdown, I managed to keep my cool a bit more, but I still pretty much jumped them.

"The Two Gallants!!" OK, so I didn't really keep my cool. "I love you!" OK, not at all.

"What the fuck are you doing here, on the Holloway Road?"

Both of them were utterly unfazed by the whole attack. Tyson just smiled a knowing smile as Adam replied, "Just looking for somewhere good to eat."

"I know just the place!" A bit forward, I guess, but I did. I'd been living on the Holloway Road for years, and the kitchen at Nambucca was for necessity only. If you wanted a decent feed, you needed to eat out. Nid Ting, the Thai restaurant directly opposite where we were standing talking, was a pretty good feed, if not a little pricey. But just around the corner was a banging boozer called the Landseer that did top-notch food for a reasonable price, and I had a friend who worked on the bar. So I said:

"I know a banging boozer, just round the corner that does top-notch food for a reasonable price. I can take you if you want."

"Sure, why not," Adam said, and off we went.

Now I know what you're thinking; this isn't a blag. Having a drink with someone you admire is very nice, but it's not a blag. You're right. The blag comes later. That evening Adam, Tyson and I hit it off and became friends. We stayed until the pub shut and then I took them around the corner to Nambucca to show them what we had going on there. It turned out that they were in town to do a show at The Scala in Kings Cross the following evening. We arranged for them to play a late-night after-show party at Nambucca too, and it was agreed that I could support them. I only went out for some cigarettes, and somehow I'd landed myself a support show with my favourite band, but this still isn't the blag. The blag came the following day, which happened to be my girlfriend's birthday. The show at The Scala was amazing, they sorted me some guestlist, and they were better live than I had ever imagined. We all headed back to Nambucca en masse, and Naumbucca did what it was good at, hosting a fucking mental night. High from my new-found friendship, the gig I'd played and a cocktail of drugs, I somehow gathered the confidence to convince the Two Gallants to help me out of a jam: the fact that I'd forgotten to get my girlfriend a present for her birthday.

The following day, early afternoon myself and my girlfriend were lying in bed. I rolled a joint and said, "Maybe we should listen to some Two Gallants?"

At that moment, the Two Gallants walked into our bedroom. Adam had his guitar, and Tyson had an old Quality Street metal tin and some drumsticks.

"Hello, and thank you for coming. We're the Two Gallants!" said Adam, talking as if he were walking on stage to a room filled with people. They took their place at the end of the bed and started to play.

It was fucking beautiful. Our favourite band, at the end of our bed, playing our favourite songs. I'd taken the liberty of giving the boys a setlist of our personal favourites. They did the whole thing entirely professionally, with no laughing or awkwardness. It was a performance, and it was breathtaking. After playing our favourite songs, we gave them the biggest applause two people could muster, and they left. Boom. That was the blag, getting a personalised gig for my girlfriend's birthday, at the end of our bed. That's a blag for sure.

Over the next few years, I saw a lot of Two Gallants, both in London and San Francisco. I also travelled out to mainland Europe to catch them playing and got to support them a few more times too. They are wonderful human beings. It's good to know that people whose music you adore are good people, should you be lucky enough to meet them. For me, that's important. I'd like to think that if I like someone's music the way I did theirs, then I have a reasonably decent understanding of who they are and what they stand for. I guess we don't often get to find that out, but on this occasion, I did, and I wasn't let down. Quite the opposite. They say never meet your heroes? Who are they anyway? And what do they know?

Do they know what a blag is? Do I? My intention of this chapter was to try and explain what exactly it is. To define it. But I guess it's harder to explain than it is to do. I believe in the blag though, and I'm still blagging it to this day, like a singer who can't really sing or someone who got a C in GCSE English writing a book, even writing two. Stick with me on this book, and I'll tell you about my most recent blag. It's a big one. I believe in luck too, if such a thing is even possible, and for what it's worth, I'm superstitious. So whatever you're doing, whatever the backdrop, stay lucky. Don't walk under ladders, don't open umbrellas inside, salute the magpies, cross your fingers, always wish on shooting stars, and if you have to: blag it.

THE BULLSHIT

Hopefully, this is a positive book. I'm a positive person, and I thought it'd be fun to share some of my stories in this format. I'm not here to criticise, have a whinge or to talk politics. To be honest, I couldn't see the point. I'm happy to sing what could be referred to as 'political' songs, that's just because I speak my mind without any filter, but overall my songs are about putting a little bit of good out into the world, however little it might do for the good of the world.

That said, sometimes you've just gotta call Bullshit. And that's what I want to talk about in this chapter. My sense of the Bullshit started at a young age. In my early teens, I got a few spots on my face, as teenagers do. Nothing too drastic, but in the mind of a 13-year-old going through puberty, a relatively big deal. Of course, I knew exactly what I needed because neatly placed in the advert breaks of *The Fresh Prince of Bel Air*, the answer was handed to me on a plate. Special soap for dealing with spots: it was called Biactol. Simple. So with three small spots on my face, I went down to Boots and bought myself a bottle. By the time I'd got halfway through the bottle, I had five spots, so I used more soap when I washed. By the time I'd finished the bottle, I had ten, and so I needed something more potent. The next level of super special soap designed for eradicating spots was called Oxy 10. I bought a bottle of that. It was to be used alongside Biactol rather than instead of it. Now I was rubbing two different chemical formulas into my face twice a day, and the spots were multiplying. To be honest, I'm not sure how long this would have gone on. It could have lasted my whole life if an intervention wasn't made. That invention came from Mel, the older sister of my friend Curt. She was incredibly beautiful and, in my eyes at the time, a sort of goddess. I didn't even dare talk to her. She existed in a whole different reality, three school years above my own. But I did spend a fair bit of time around Curt's house. One day after I'd been to Boots to purchase my Oxy 10, I'd left it out on Curts kitchen table, and Mel walked into the kitchen. I sat in silent awe, as Mel calmly picked up the bottle.

"Don't use this stuff. It only makes things worse. If you want to get rid of your spots, just use the soap your mum already has next to the sink. Wash with hot water, followed by cold water. Stay away from this. It's a sham."

Mel talked to me! I couldn't believe it. I didn't actually respond at all. I just stood staring at her completely in awe, probably with my mouth wide open, as she made herself a drink and then walked out of the kitchen. She talked to me, looked right at me. Not only that, but it seemed the goddess even threw down a scrap of wisdom, some advice. I didn't really think too much about what she'd said, but when I got home, I threw my new bottle of fancy zit soap away and used the communal bathroom bar of soap that had been there throughout the whole ordeal. As instructed: hot water, cold water.

Two weeks later, my spots had all but gone. Sure, I got more over the next few years, right through my life, in fact, but they came, and they went without any fanfare and without any trips to Boots. In the days and weeks that followed my encounter with Mel, I thought hard about the reality of a company that sells soap to teenagers with spots. Why on earth would they want to sell a soap that works? That just means they won't buy it anymore. It makes much more sense to confuse these poor kids into buying more of their product by giving them more spots and force-feeding them well-thought-out advertising. I began to realise that there are powers at work in the world that will screw you over for their own gain, spouting all kinds of Bullshit. I became extremely distrustful of all advertising, as I still am to this day. In the words of my dear friend Switters:

"The more advertising I see, the less I want to buy."

Hand in hand with my new found scepticism of advertising came a widespread suspicion of television. This was fully confirmed some years later, around 1998, when I went to the filming of the popular TV chat show of the time: *The Vanessa Show.* I went with my college class as part of our B-Tech National Diploma in Performing Arts, a bullshit name for a qualification if ever there was one. Our whole class jumped on board a coach, and we headed from Braintree to Norwich in the nearby county of Norfolk. We arrived at Anglia Television studios that morning, where they gathered up the whole class into a room to explain a few bits.

Vanessa was a studio-based chat show filmed in front of a live audience. The general premise was this: seemingly ordinary people that lived troubled or strange lives would sit on a couch and be interviewed by the professional celebrity journalist Vanessa Feltz. The studio audience, chosen at random, were supposed to represent ordinary people who didn't live particularly troubled or strange lives. Or if they did, they wouldn't admit it. The show dealt with real human emotions in a cartoon manner, from single mothers to anorexic teenagers, shoplifters and sex addicts. It was looking for opposing views on these issues, getting people to battle it out; nothing like a good argument to keep the masses entertained.

They didn't need to explain this to my class and me. We all watched the show avidly and knew the score. But what they did explain to us was that they would be filming two shows on the day we were visiting. One in the morning and one in the afternoon. Most of us would have the morning to ourselves to walk around the wonderful city of Norwich, and then we'd come back at 2pm to be part of the studio audience. But while they had us here, they explained that they'd had a little problem. It seemed that some of the guests for that morning's show, who were supposed to sit on the sofa and get the conversations flowing, hadn't shown up. They wondered if anyone in the room felt like they could fit into the category, "You're so slick it makes me sick". To the ears of a class of 19-year-old performing arts students, that sentence could be roughly translated to "Does anyone here want to be on TV?" Hands flew up, 90% of the class, all pick-me pick-me eyes and little waves from their raised hands. The show producer scanned the room, then pointed out five of my classmates. "You five come with me, the rest of you go and enjoy your morning. We'll see you for this afternoon's filming of Vanessa." She did some little jazz hands as she said the show's name.

What happened next I didn't witness first hand. I was told reliably by each of the five classmates the following day. The producer took them to a back room, flattered them for a bit, then made them all sign some kind of confidentiality agreement. She then devised a storyline between the five classmates that bore absolutely no relation to reality. According to the producer, Aaron had been in a long term relationship with Kirsty, and Kirtsy had been cheating on him with Roger. Roger had also been sleeping with Gemma, who was going out with Paul. Neither Gemma, Kirsty, or Roger felt any kind of remorse. Basically, Roger was an arsehole, sleeping with other peoples girlfriends and then bragging about it. In fact, he was a lovely guy, not a cheat at all, but he was a great actor and a budding one at that. He took on the part and strolled out onto the sofa to get the goat of the whole country.

This I did see first hand, on TV about three months later, when the show was aired. The crowd hated Roger, the cheat, the liar, the arrogant arsehole. There was outrage, and there were arguments, both from the crowd and the sofa at the front. It was riveting TV. But it was Bullshit, piles and piles of Bullshit. And everyone believed it. Roger couldn't walk down the street for months without people shouting at him or hissing at him. His aunt disowned him after his appalling behaviour; he told her it was all an act, but she refused to believe it. It was Vanessa. This was real life.

I'd tell people about the story, and they'd often say, "Yeah, but not every episode of Vanessa is a bunch of coerced performing arts students. Some of them are real people." That may well be the case, but who fucking cares? If they're ready to lie through their teeth at the drop of a hat just to keep the show rolling, then we shouldn't believe a word they say. We should call it what it is. At the same time, across the pond, Jerry Springer was kicking off - in more ways than one. In a kind of worship of stupidity or feeling of empowerment through judgement, reality TV was here to stay, and it was Bullshit. Still is.

After that, my Bullshit detector was on full force. I started looking for things devoid of Bullshit. I found solace in a few people, places and things, probably most notably drugs. Nobody ever advertised drugs to you. Quite the opposite, the establishment and all figures of authority just said "no" and pretty much refused to give any more information than that. Yes, I guess drugs were glamorised by the music I was listening to and the books I was reading, and there would have been an element of peer pressure, but I was a strong-minded teenager. I made my own decisions. None that I regret either, that tab of acid that I dropped when I was 17 kicked into gear the person I am today. It was one of the most insane nights of my life and still the most explicit memory I hold of that time. I can remember the whole evening. I only took acid again a handful of times in my life, and they were many years later in completely different circumstances. The experience of tripping and the many other high times of my youth elevated my sense of Bullshit, my distrust of the system, and they also led me to people and places that tried their best to exist outside of it.

Braintree didn't have a free party scene, and by free party, I mean illegal rave. But there were enough people in Braintree who wanted one, and huge car convoys regularly travelled up to Luton for Exodus Raves. At the time, being into 'guitar music', I presumed these weren't for me and was happy with my gigs and festivals fix. Some of my mates in college would play techno and drum & bass in their cars while we sat and smoked weed. This further led me to believe that raving wasn't for me. Until, of course, I went to one. I was walking home from the pub one night, and the convoy of cars happened to drive by. My friend Chris pulled over and pretty much ordered me to get in the car. I'd had a few and got in without question: another great decision. The rave was nothing like I'd ever witnessed at a gig or a festival. It was completely free of charge and felt like the polar opposite of an advert or a shopping centre. I fell in love and went to many raves over the next few years, drawn by a lack of advertising, loud music and doing it for the fuck of it. If I'm completely honest, I also witnessed people so detached from the system that they'd lost the plot, which was quite an important sight. There's no point fucking the system if you end up fucking yourself in the process.

Still a wide-eyed kid in many respects, I hadn't actually put much thought into this world view that I was forming. I was very much just following my nose, going with my gut and doing what felt right to me. Apart from that, what can anyone do? Growing up, I had zero interest in politics; it didn't even come into it. We didn't talk about it at home. None of my friends had opinions on the matter. It felt like something that existed in a different universe entirely and bore no relation to me and mine. Sure, I knew who Marget Thatcher was, and Tony Blair, but they were merely names in a newspaper that looked like Bullshit to me. That's probably a testament to the good politics of the 90's. I guess if you're healthy, happy and don't feel like you're getting screwed over, someone must be doing something right. Right? Well, right or wrong, that all ended with the Iraq war.

I might not have had a stance on current politics, but I knew that war was bad, and I didn't want to be part of one. So I went along to the 2003 anti-war march in London. It was part of a coordinated day of protests worldwide and hailed as the largest such event in human history; the message was simple: stop the war. I basically saw it as the world calling out Bullshit, and when the powers that be ignored us completely and the war started, my world view shifted. It became clear to me that the Bullshit leads all the way to the top, and then some.

I didn't really want to be anti-war though, I mean, of course, I was, but it just seemed a strange way of putting it. Why be anti-anything? I'd much rather be pro-peace.

For a long time, I would have referred to myself as an anti-capitalist; reading Namoi Klein's *No Logo* shone a light on my life. Finally, someone was talking some sense. Someone was explaining to me why I saw Bullshit everywhere and why it was happening. And it came down to money; money and power. People were being screwed by the system big time. I stopped eating McDonald's in an instant and tried to live a life that opposed the evil powers all around us, but you know what? It was fucking impossible. Without turning into the screwball at the rave that had lost his place in society, all I did was fill my boots with big ideas, with no way of executing them. Capitalism still reigns free and is stamping and stomping around the place, wrecking the planet and dividing the people, more than ever before and here I sit writing about it on an Apple laptop. So what do I know? The world is a confusing place, always has been. And as my friend Paul Thorn says:

"Whatever you believe, you might be wrong."

These days, I've almost come around full circle, going back to following my nose, going with my gut and doing what feels right to me. I can still smell the Bullshit from a mile away, and I would still never set foot in a McDonald's or ever consider eating the poison they present as food.

To this day, I'm still tricked by the Bullshit, and its never-ending nonsense. Wetherspoons pubs. Fuck me, I used to love them. While living and working and breathing Nambucca, a fully independent pub, my favourite place to drink was the Spoons on Holloway Road. A beautiful, historic building filled with wonderful characters, generous opening hours and the cheapest pint around. It was amazing. When I started touring, going to a Spoons felt like taking my local on the road, I knew what to expect and how much to pay. I was a big fan. Now look at the place: eating up other pubs at a drastic rate, killing competition, doing backhanders with the government, cashing in on tragedy, treating their staff like shit and buying up the only real boozers left. It's like a drunk driver crashing a stolen car into our culture, and it's not something I can get behind. It's Bullshit.

I think what I'm trying to say is: don't believe the Bullshit. But I've said that before, many times in fact, and please don't get me wrong: not only do I live in this society, but I wholeheartedly partake in it. As mentioned, I'm writing this book on a top of the range computer, and no doubt you're holding your copy because I advertised it to you in some way or another. I recognise that this same system has meant I can live a life of luxury compared to many lives that came before. But that doesn't make it right, and everywhere I look now, it seems that it's falling apart because it's unsustainable. The power, the money, and the greed is wrecking the world, and everybody knows this to be true. But somehow, the Bullshit reigns supreme. We're living without a shared vision; as a society and as the human race as a whole, we need a story that we all believe in. One that rings true for everyone. We need to find a model that isn't governed by greed. I'm not saying that's going to be easy, but seeing the Bullshit for what it is, is as good a place to start as any. I can't help but feel that the vast problems we face as the human race, be it climate collapse, poverty, unhappiness, war and inequality, are all down to a society that is governed by greed and lies, built on Bullshit, and sometimes you've just got to call it out. Because it stinks.

But hang on, didn't this book start out with a Bullshit story? Isn't a blag just Bullshit in a different form? Isn't the next chapter and bunch of get rich quick schemes? Am I a walking contradiction? Can you smell that?

GET RICH QUICK

This chapter isn't a story, just some ideas I wanted to share with you. After spilling my guts about spots and anti-capitalist fantasies, I'm worried that you think I might be taking myself a little too seriously, so I'll level out a little. There's nothing wrong with a little contradiction, and so in this chapter, I'll share some get rich quick schemes with you. These are ideas I've been banging on about for ages, always saying I'm going to do them, but have never gotten around to. Maybe they were different paths my life could have taken, maybe safety nets for the day that people stop listening to my songs, maybe I've didn't had the gusto to deliver them, or maybe it's just me talking shit. Now it's time for you to decide, because I've had enough of talking about them and not doing anything, so I'll share them with you. Maybe you'll put them into action. If you do, don't you forget about little old me now, will you?

SPLIFFBOAT

You get a barge on the canals in Amsterdam and decorate the thing as a giant spliff, complete with a glowing red cherry that lights up every time you rev the engine. You then have two Spliff Stops, where you pick people up and drop them off. You then charge people €10 for a ten minute trip between the stops, smoking a spliff on Spliffboat. You drop them off at the Spliff Stop where everyone gets off, and you pick up the next lot of eager spliff loving tourists. You spend all day getting high on the canals of Amsterdam, making a shit ton of money while you're at it. Sorted.

GIG DATE

This is a dating app based on selling tickets to gigs. You set up the app and the website. It's like other dating sites, but it's all based around music. People set up a profile consisting of a couple of pictures, and then a list of bands and music they like, and a list of gigs they've been to recently. People can then go onto the app and say what gigs they'd be interested in going to, they get matched with someone who wants to go to the same gig, and if you both agree, the app sorts out the tickets, and you arrange to meet, either outside or at the show.

This works because gigs are an easy place for a first date. There is instantly a connection through the shared love of the same music. There's plenty to talk about and it's a great ice breaker, but you don't have to talk if you don't want to - you can watch the show. If you're not feeling it, gigs are an easy place to walk away from someone too. Stand on the other side of the room, and you'll never see that person again. People will love it because it has more soul than dating apps that are just about image and ego. Gig promoters will love it because it's their job to sell tickets, so you'll be doing that for them. You'll sell it to a big tech company for a shit-ton of money, and more than that, you'll be bringing people together and helping them find love. Sorted.

THE ROCK N ROLLER

You build a device that can add wheels to any hard guitar case. If you go back to an airport in the 1980's, everyone was carrying their suitcases, entirely off the ground. At that point, nobody had thought of putting wheels on the things. Whoever thought of putting wheels on suitcases, I bet they're well and truly sorted. But nobody has thought of doing it for guitars, not yet anyway. Make something that you can attach to guitar cases and sell them to weak-armed guitar players the world over. Sorted.

CLIPPER USA

Did you know they don't have clippers in the states? Fucking crazy. Maybe you've never even heard of a clipper. The greatest lighter in the world, for sure, a true classic, but for some reason bound to British shores. Export that thing. I've never met an American who wasn't impressed with a clipper lighter, and that's just one country. There's probably loads of places that don't have clippers; import them, sell them, sorted. Well, sort of sorted. This is a very old scheme; nowadays I'd probably note that they are made from plastic and should therefore either be updated or eradicated. On top of that, I'm not even sure if anyone smokes anymore. But, you know, it was a good idea at the time.

CARTENT

Ever slept in the back of a car? It's uncomfortable, right? Even if the car is parked, and you can dangle your legs out, you just can't get comfortable. That's why you invent a simple device that folds out from the backseat, through the open door and, supported by your own bodyweight, turns the car into a little tent. Who needs a camper van, when you've got Cartent? It's a niche market, but it's out there and it wants a good night's sleep. Sorted.

TOAST

You want to go to festivals for free? You want to make some dough? So you make Toast. A festival food stall that sells nothing but toast. 50p for two slices of toast with butter, served on a piece of kitchen roll. You don't sell anything else, no water, no cups of tea, nothing. Not even jam or any condiments, just toast. This is to your benefit because you can make and serve toast quickly and everyone is going to want some. Everyone loves toast. And 50p! At a festival, where food prices have risen to the point of absolute idiocy, you'll be selling toast every minute the festival grounds are open. For every slice of toast you sell, you've made enough to buy a loaf of bread and a tub of butter. Everyone wins. Sorted.

MESSING WITH TEXAS

Regardless of my feelings about McDonalds or capitalism in general, I've always had a huge fondness for America. Raised on a substantial and fulfilling diet of American music, books, TV and film, I've always had a special place in my heart for the US of A.

I'm writing this in early January 2021. An extraordinary time for the self-appointed land of the free. Just last night, the Capitol was stormed by smiling Nazis in fancy dress. Somehow, a group of around a thousand sore losers, waving flags and insults, stomped into one of the American government's central buildings, hyped up on conspiracy, nationalism and bigotry. Five or six years ago, an event like this would have been unthinkable. I mean, it still seems fucking nuts, even if just for the fact that the US spent $700 billion on defence in 2020 and somehow can't keep a mob of loud mouth white supremacists out of the building where they make the laws. Maybe the worrying fact is that they didn't want to keep them out. As I said, a strange time. The world seems to be moving faster than ever. Trump has gone, but the scars remain, and I feel there will be much more disruption to come over the next few years. The end of a civilisation is never a pretty sight after all. But that's not why we're here, is it? We're here to fondly walk down memory lane. The first time I crossed the pond was a trip to Florida when I was 17, which ended in disaster, so we won't linger on that now. But the second time I went was when I was 21, and it was the first time I ever went to Texas. That's when it stole my heart.

It's no surprise that I ended up harbouring such affection for the States. It's pretty much in my blood. Both my folks are obsessed with the place. I know that if someone from outside of the UK has a strong connection to my homeland, they're referred to as an Anglophile. I'm not aware of a similar word used for people who love America, but if it exists, then that's what my folks are. My dad, especially. He's a huge country music fan, who likes big gestures and open roads. Dad's got several tattoos proclaiming his love, including an American flag. He had it done on the cheap though, and they couldn't fit all the stars in, but it doesn't seem to bother him. He's also got a few tattoos referencing his all-time favourite singer, Jimmy Buffett. A musician so American that outside of the continent, no one has even heard of him, but inside he's as well known as Madonna or Elvis. On dad's right arm, pride of place, he has the outline of his favourite state: Texas.

When living at home, it didn't feel like my folks were waiting for me to leave - far from it. But when I did move out of the family home aged 19, it only took them a couple of months to explain that they were selling the house I'd grown up in, a semi-detached three-bedroom house on the outskirts of Braintree in Essex, and buying a smaller semi-detached two-bedroom house on the other side of town. They were planning to rent the house out, and with the money they'd made from the sale and the rent, they were going to 'move' to America.

'Move' was a big word, and they knew full well they couldn't legally move there for good, but they bought one-way tickets, and the plan was not to have a plan. They'd come back when they were ready, and if an opportunity arose to stay, perhaps they would take it. I think the preference would have been them buying some kind of Winnebago for the trip, but alas, there was no budget for that, so they bought a car and a tent on arrival and travelled the country, staying in State Parks, KOA's and cheap motels, visiting places that had been referenced in dad's favourite songs, and the big tourist sites of the country. Obviously, they had a whale of a time, no doubt making lots of friends along the way, for that has always been their way. A few months into the trip, they settled in a small fishing town in Southeast Texas called Anahuac. How they ended up there escapes me, but somehow this tiny little Texas town became their home. And they loved it. If they could have had their way, I think they would have stayed, but the reality of visas and not being able to work started to dawn on them, and when my nan, on my mum's side, fell ill, they decided to call it a day and head back to Blighty. They knew they had friends for life in Anahuac though, and promised to return, and they did exactly that. Six months later, we all went. A full McAllister family trip to Anahuac, TX, for Christmas and New Year 2002.

I was 21 at the time. Living in London, working at The Fortress, and, as I've mentioned, life was a party. But I was happy to spend some time with my folks and my brother, and intrigued about this new home my folks had discovered. The pace of life in Anahuac was the polar opposite of what I was used to, but the place was fascinating. Most of the town felt like a beefed-up trailer park, but with loads of open space - loads of beautiful trees intersected with pretty brutal buildings and big roads for big cars. My parents were like local celebrities of the town. Everybody called them 'The British Couple'. On arrival, we stopped at the local shop and, seconds after we walked in, a lady from behind the checkout yelled at the top of her voice, "Y'all...The British couple are back!" Everyone in the shop was soon huddled around us, my folks knew everyone by name, and I could see that they loved the big homecoming. After that, we got shuffled around a lot, visiting friends and being introduced to half the town. Outside one of their friend's trailers, someone handed me a gun for the first time in my life, and I nearly shot my big toe off, missing it by about 10 centimetres, I reckon. I had no idea the thing was going to be loaded. Everybody thought it was funny as fuck. "Welcome to Texas," they kept saying. My brother and I also got a ride in some dude's little biplane, which was epic. Again, just someone they knew in town; everyone was keen to show the English couple's kids a good time. And it was great. However, the plan was to stay for two weeks. All my folk's friends were my folk's age, and as you'd imagine, that well ran dry quite quickly for a 21-year-old.

There was one bar in town, a sweet little joint on the water called The Channel Marker. This is where we drank. I actually did a little gig there, which is odd because this was years before I'd ever step on stage and call myself Beans on Toast. I'd played in bands and had been on stage many times, of course, and had tons of songs written, but I'd never played a solo gig with an acoustic guitar before. To be honest, I think I was just trying to make *something* happen and looking back now, it worked.

One of the chaps in the bar that night bought me a drink after I'd played a few songs. His name was Alan, and he was a Texas cowboy. Whilst having a drink, we got to talking (as the cowboys say), and I explained that I was looking for a bit of life on my trip, or at least some people my age. "Y'all need to get your ass to Austin," He told me. I agreed, and by the end of the night, he'd agreed to drive me. A plan had been laid down that on Boxing Day (which was a few days away from when we were talking), Alan would drive my brother and me to Austin. It was a four hour drive, but he didn't seem to mind. My old man would then come to pick us up a few days later and bring us back in time for the big New Year's party at the pop-up honky-tonk in town. "What are you going to do when you get to Austin?" my Mum asked. I explained the plan was not to have a plan, and she understood.

Fast forward through a Country & Western cowboy Christmas in the sunshine and a four hour trek in Alan's pick up, and we're dropped off on 6th Street in Austin. Alan wished us his best, tipped his hat, and off he went. It's just me and my brother Kes. Kes looked at me. I looked at the closest bar and walked in. The bar was empty, save for the bartender.

"Jay?" says the bartender, almost instantly. I don't recognise the guy and can't really believe it, but, "Yeah..." I reply, doing a bad job at hiding the confusion on my face. "You work at the Barfly in Camden, don't you? You stagemanaged my band there a few months ago." The name of the band escapes me now, but he told me the band name and I did recognise him; he was the drummer in a great band I'd seen and thinking about it, yeah, they were from Texas.

"That's a fucking trip man, what on earth are you doing in Austin?"

"Looking for a drink!" I said, and as he poured us a couple of beers, I told him about our story, and how we were in Austin for a few days, with some money in our pockets but no plan of where to go or where to stay.

"Well, these beers are on the house, and I get off work at 8 tonight. I'm going to a party. You folks should come." Austin. I love you already.

We didn't actually leave the bar until 8pm that night. My brother and I just sat drinking, catching up all afternoon. He took the whole thing in his stride, as is his way. He took the events of the next few days completely in his stride as well, didn't bat an eyelid, and the next few days got pretty wild.

On the way to the party, the bartender explained the deal of where we were heading. The party was on the edge of town in a derelict cinema that had recently been taken over by some kind of community art collective, and they were raising funds to do the place up. It was $20 on entry, and once you'd paid that, you could drink as much as you liked. It sounded unreal to me, and going by how much I liked to drink, more than a bargain. I feel bad for not remembering the bartender's name or the name of his band (who were really good). He obviously played a crucial part in my introduction to Austin, but once we were in the party, I never saw him again.

I still didn't really believe that drinks would be free once we'd paid our $20 admission. I paid it happily though, and walked straight to the bar and said, "Can I really drink as much as I like for free now?" and then she appeared. She must have been crouching down behind the bar, because she popped up like a jack-in-the-box. "PG tips, PG tips, PG tips," she kept repeating in a pretty poor attempt at a Hugh Grant-style English accent. She was beautiful - absolutely stunning. Like a movie star, but from a cool as fuck Tarantino movie. She was dressed to the nines, whatever that means, she looked amazing, and she completely knocked me off my feet. It was like I'd been hit with a stun gun or something. In one hand, she held a red plastic cup with a white trim, the kind I'd seen in every party in the movies, but never in real life. With her other hand, she then produced a keg of beer and plonked it on the bar in front of me. "Yes, my English friend, tonight we drink for free." She poured a beer, necked the whole thing, then poured another one and gave it to me. "My name's Juliana," she said in a thick Texas accent. "And I have a thing for English boys."

She was well out of my league, that was for sure. She was also a lot older than me. I've never been a good judge of age, but I was guessing early thirties, and remember I was merely 21 at the time. On a different level, she was the kind of woman that I'd fantasised about but had never had any contact with - not that I let that stop me. I necked the beer in one, put the cup down on the bar and said, "My name's Jay, and I've got a thing for Texan girls."

"Let me show you around," she said, and she leapt over the bar, picked up the keg, and walked into the party. Wow. I followed. We drank, we danced, we kissed, we did coke, and we talked each other's socks off. It turned out she'd helped organise the party. Her friends were part of the art collective that had recently taken over the space. It really was an incredible space too, a '50s cinema and concert hall that had been driven into the ground and was just working its way back up, the very first tingles of what would become mass gentrification for the city. When the lights came on, and the people left, we stayed, part of the crew, beer still flowing. At some point during the night, I'd explained that we didn't have anywhere to stay, and she just said, "Yes, you do PG Tips," - that was now my nickname - "you're staying with me." "And my brother?" I responded.

"There's room for everyone."

And so when the end of the night did actually come around, long after the general public had left the party, Juliana walked behind the bar, grabbed another keg of beer, and we left. Taking a fresh keg of beer with us we hitched a ride in a bright red mustang convertible. On our way back to her house, she looked across at me and said, "How are you liking Austin so far?"I stood up in the convertible, put both hands high up in the sky and felt the warm Texas air wash over me, like I'd seen in so many movies before, and shouted, "I LOVE IT!!!"

For the next three days, we stayed at Juliana's, did cocaine and fucked each other's brains out. Sorry to kiss and tell, but that's how it went down. And it was wild. She had an epic house on the edge of the city, complete with a front porch, a swing in the yard, and the Stars & Stripes hanging proudly in the driveway. Was this the American dream? We only left the house of an evening to go drinking around the city. She knew all the best bars and clubs, and had friends all over town. One night we were out at a club, and someone walked up to me and offered me a free pack of cigarettes.

"Would you like a free pack of Camel Lights?" she said. What the fuck was going on? "Yes, of course, I would!" I got really excited and asked why on earth anyone would be walking around giving out free packs of Camels in a nightclub. It was a promotion thing, the girl said, as if that was obvious. I realised that it would be an excellent promotion for cigarettes. They're trying to get people hooked, after all. It would almost certainly have been illegal back at home, but we were not at home now, were we? I told the girl giving away cigarettes that she had the easiest job in the world, and she replied, "My boss would like to speak to you." Which was kind of weird, because she didn't have any time to confer with her boss, but she pointed to the corner and said, "Her name is Big Sue, go and tell her what you told me."

Sue lived up to her name. Easily the size of two average humans, maybe two and a half. She was sitting in a corner booth in the back of the club. She was alone, taking up half the booth, drinking directly from a pitcher, with an ashtray piled like a mountain of what I could only gather were Camel Light butts. I walked over.

Five minutes later, she'd offered me a job - the easiest job in the world, giving away packs of cigarettes to drunk people in nightclubs. I could work as much or as little as I liked, seven nights a week if it suited me. I'd get $70 a night, free entry to every club in town, and as many Camel Lights as I could smoke while doing it. I'd also be able to keep all tips, and the whole thing was entirely off the books, cash work. She didn't give two shits that I couldn't legally work in the country. She just said that with enthusiasm like mine, I'd be the best she had. I took her number and told her I'd think about it. Was this the American Dream?

The following morning, my dad came to pick us up, back on 6th Street, where Alan had dropped us off a few days before and a whole lifetime ago. I can only guess my brother had also had a good time, judging by the fact he was wearing a knee-length black fur coat - not his usual style. At all. But as I said, he'd taken the whole ride in his stride.

The last night at Juliana's, we did the same as the two before, and in-between the action, I commented about moving to Texas for good, giving out packs of fags for a living. "Y'all can stay here anytime you please, PG tips," she said.

It wasn't like she was offering that because she saw anything happening between us, I could feel that. She kind of used me as a plaything. I felt that too, in more ways than one. That was more than fine with me. She was just wild and free and generous, and If I wanted to stay, then I could.

We were back in Anahuac just in time for New Year's Eve, when the town put it's glad rags on, and gathered at the town hall to drink Coors Light, wobble around some line-dancing routines and see in the New Year with the bang of a few gunshots. It was great; I'd had such a mental few days in Austin that the trip was now a success. I was happy to be back with my folks and hang out with their Texan buddies. In the early hours of the morning, me and mum went down by the water and had what turned into a bit of a drunken heart to heart. I was hammered by this point, and I said to mum, only half-joking, that I might stay. Go back to Austin and live there for a bit, see how it plays out.

"Don't be stupid," my mum said, "You don't have a job or anywhere to stay, or a visa. And what about all the fantastic things you've been telling me about in London? Are you going to just leave them?" Obviously, she was right, and I didn't really intend to stay in Texas, but it seemed strange of her to say it like this. Didn't she want to live here herself? If she had the chance to stay, wouldn't she take it? I explained that I did, in fact, have a job, and somewhere to stay and maybe even a girlfriend... of sorts - who knew what could happen? I tried to convince her it was a good idea in a kind of knee-jerk reaction to her telling me not to be stupid, and almost convinced myself in the exchange, even though I was, in fact, being stupid. Then I drank some more.

I was woken up early, with a hangover by Tracy, one of my folk's friends, who'd been putting the family up for the last part of the trip. We were flying home that evening. My plan was to sleep all day, but Tracy said there was someone on the phone… "For me?" Confused and blurry, I got up and stumbled to the phone. As I put it to my ear, I could hear Juliana's voice.

"This buttfuck town ain't easy to find PG Tips."

My memory came flashing back like a Texas tornado. After the conversation with my mum, I'd drunk a few shots with Alan and then called Juliana from a payphone. I'd told her I wanted to stay, to stay with her. To make a life in Texas. I would imagine it was quite the speech, even if it was the booze talking. Juliana, it seemed, had got up first thing and was coming in her red convertible to collect me. I needed to collect my thoughts. A fork in the road. Two different lives ahead of me. I made a sober decision quickly and apologised.

"Juliana, I'm going home today. I'm sorry. I've messed you around; I think I just needed to know that I could stay if I wanted to, that my own little piece of the American dream was there for the taking should I want to take it. But I don't. It was the whiskey talking. Thank you for everything, but this is goodbye."

"Don't worry your pretty little head about it," said Juliana. "It's been fun. Y'all come back to Austin sometime. I know you will." And she hung up. Wow. What a woman. I headed back to bed, woke up a few hours later, and the McAllisters headed back home. To our actual home this time. All of us together.

Juliana was right. I did go back to Austin, though not for a while. My next visit was six years later, in 2008, for the South-By-Southwest (SXSW) music festival. Lots had happened at home in that time, and by 2008 I was running a big successful indie night in the West End of London, running a music venue on the Holloway Road, managing a band called The Holloways, and singing songs under the name Beans on Toast.

The opportunity to go to Texas came through The Holloways. We'd just signed to a big US label, had a top 20 single in the UK, and had plans to break America. SXSW was a kind of rite of passage, as well as being the world's biggest music industry hobnob. At the time, indie music in London was huge. It was going off: incredible bands, young record labels, rammed club nights. On the nights I wasn't putting on a gig, I'd generally be at one. It was a really exciting time. And everyone was going to SXSW. Not just the bands, but the booking agents, A&R, journalists, promoters. Pretty much everyone I knew at the time was heading out to Texas for a week of booze, barbeque, bands and as it turned out... blow.

The Holloways had been offered an official slot at the festival, and between myself, the agent and the label, we'd organised an insanely gruelling schedule for the band, which is how to do SXSW. There's so many people, so many venues, and so much going on that bands are running around non-stop, playing gigs in restaurants, shops, houses and hotel lobbies, as well as big gig venues and outdoor festival stages. It is an event like no other. Once I knew I had my ticket and delegate pass sorted, I wangled myself some Beans on Toast gigs as well. Obviously.

One of those gigs was a show at an Irish bar just off 6th Street. The gig had found me; someone had messaged me about it on Myspace (if you don't remember Myspace, it was like Facebook before Facebook, with fewer photos and more music). The venue was putting on a showcase for English singers and wondered if I wanted to play. Yes, of course I did. A few messages went back and forth on Myspace to lock the gig in. A week before I set off, I asked if we could switch to email, as I wasn't sure if I'd be able to access Myspace on my travels (this was the age of blackberry, pre-smartphones). A few days later, an email about the gig landed on my chunky little handheld device, with information about the gig, and the sender of the email: it was from Juliana.

Fuck me! I'd obviously thought about Juliana when planning the trip, as I had for a long time after returning from my holiday all those years ago. But I had no way of getting in touch with her. It turned out I'd been messaging her on Myspace this whole time. Back when we'd met, I wasn't playing as Beans on Toast, and at the time had put out no photos of myself, just music. So I was guessing she had no idea it was me either. As I said, lots had changed for me since our last trip, most notably the fact that now I was in a serious relationship. I mailed her back, excited, and asked if she remembered me.

"PG Tips! Of course, I remember you. What a coincidence," she replied. She too was in a relationship now. "Don't fret it," she told me, "it'll be great to see you again." She then said she was also doing a few shows at her house, and if I wanted another gig, then I could swing by and play at a barbeque in her back garden.

She still had a thing for English boys, it seemed. Her current boyfriend was English, and she was also personally arranging an evening of music by English performers. Both gigs she set up were wicked. It was amazing to see her again. I also managed to get back a hoodie that I'd left at her house six years before. Crazy shit. The festival itself was as good as I'd imagined, if not better. Probably my favourite thing about it was it lasted a whole week. Festivals in the UK usually last a weekend, the big ones stretching out to four days, but this was seven days and seven days full power, non-stop. I asked Juliana where to buy coke, and she said these days she didn't touch the stuff, but that I shouldn't have too much trouble tracking it down...

She wasn't wrong. The following day I was on 6th Street alone, flipping through the schedule planning my day. I had the afternoon free. I'd been to a bunch of Holloways shows already, including the important label showcase and official festival show. They had loads more gigs, but I wasn't necessarily needed. My next Beans gig was the following day, that was my official gig of the festival, and I wasn't really expecting much from it. It was early days for me as an artist, especially across the pond. Yes, I knew shit loads of people at the festival, every other person I bumped into I knew from back home, but they were all industry folks, and as much as they were friends, or colleagues even, none of them gave a shit about Beans on Toast. Fair do's, it's not really music that suits the business, I've always kind of liked it like that. All the music biz folk from London were running around trying to catch the next big thing or the hot new act. They weren't going to come and see me. So be it; the whole trip was on the blag, and I knew I'd enjoy the gig even if it was in an empty venue. I was having a ball at the festival, and as I said, I had a day and night free to get stuck into the festival.

"Hey mate, do you know where I can buy some coke?"

I just asked the guy standing next to me when it came into my mind; I didn't really think about it any more than that. He was just the closest person to me when I decided the best plan would be to get some sniff.

"How did you know to ask me?" the guy responded with a big smile. "Who told you about me?"

"Nobody told me anything. I'm just trying my luck."

"Well, congratulations, you're a lucky guy. I'm the biggest coke dealer in this city."

He didn't look like a coke dealer at all. He looked more like a blogger for a small underground music website, almost nerdy. But he was very sure of himself, and his smile just kept beaming.

"Great!" I said. "Let's do some coke." Trying my luck again.

"Where?"

"Here?"

We were standing at the corner of East 6th Street and Red River, a huge junction, and right in the mix of the festival. There were people fucking everywhere.

"Here?" he said.

"Sure, why not?"

I've never been a fan of hiding while doing drugs; it strikes me as a bit rude. Yes, obviously, I know they're illegal and what have you, but still. The only good drugs are the sociable ones, and hiding away isn't sociable at all. I also find that being sneaky about shit makes you look guilty; I don't feel guilty doing drugs (or I didn't, when I did do them), so I didn't look guilty. Nobody batted an eyelid. I won't list the insane places I've taken various substances in. But a street corner in the middle of all these people, for me, that was fine.

"Crazy English guy," the chap said, and pulled out the biggest bag of coke I'd ever seen in my life. Fuck, now I felt guilty, not even sure what would happen if you got caught with that much coke in Texas. They'd probably send me to the chair. The guy is a real pro though, pulls out the bag, sticks in a key and sticks the key under my nose. Bosh. It's gone. He sticks the key back in the bag to sort himself out. Before the key is anywhere near his nose, the coke hits me. Fucking hell. This is the best coke I've ever done.

At the time, my most popular song, by far, was a song called 'Coke'. It was about how I did loads of it and how everyone I knew did loads of it too. And it was a true song, or at least I thought so until I tried this coke. Now that I'd tried this, I had to question what the fuck we'd all been putting up our noses back in London all this time. I think I even let out a whoop, the kind of thing you'd expect someone to do a movie when they do a line, but never in real life.

"That's the best fucking coke I've ever had in my life! I said after my whoop, and the guy's smile got bigger and brighter. "Well, my crazy English friend, there's plenty more where that came from. This one's for you," he said as he slipped something into my pocket, "and here's my number. If you know any other crazy English folk who want some, you call me." I don't think I even responded. The coke was so fucking strong, I just stood there and wobbled my head in agreement, then after he'd disappeared, let out another little whoop.

I had a fucking mental night. The bag of coke was massive. I was basically the proud owner of the biggest bag of strongest coke I'd ever had, at a festival. As I said, I already had a lot of friends at the festival and there's nothing quite like a big bag of coke to help you make more!

I won't even try to remember the actual events of the evening, although I do remember at one point sharing a cab with James Iha from The Smashing Pumpkins after fleeing a house party because a wall fell down. I realised early on that I was in possession of way more gear than I could do before my flight home, so I went about my night giving lines away to anyone and everyone, mainly the movers and shakers of the UK music business. As is the way with that stuff, everybody wanted more. Somewhere along the way of my little gift-giving expedition, I devised a plan. Yes, I told everyone who asked, I can get more. There's plenty more where that came from, and I told everyone to meet me at 2pm the following day at Little Reds Bar, just off 6th Street. Everyone had the same feeling about this being a different breed to the London racket, and they said they would be there. I saw a fair few people making notes on their busy festival schedule, fuck whatever hot new upcoming band they were supposed to be watching. They'd be at Little Reds at 2pm for sure. If anyone else wanted some, they could head down there too, plenty more where that came from.

I didn't tell anyone that 2pm at Little Reds was actually the stage time and venue for Beans on Toast's official SXSW performance.

I turned up for my gig the following day, and the venue was rammed, almost at capacity. Full of A&R men, promoters, major label heads, journalists and hip new bands. It was perfect. I walked on stage to a collective sigh. I'd duped the lot of them. Only slightly though, as I started off my gig by saying, "If you're here for the coke, you'll have to wait until the end of the gig." And then I played my song 'Coke'. Another collective sigh, but everyone waited - every single one of them. I'd met up with my new-found friend, the now-confirmed biggest coke dealer in Austin, half an hour beforehand, and told him my plan. He'd agreed to it and came down to sort everyone out but only once my show was over. He gave me another bag for free and just said, "Crazy English Man." Was this the American Dream?

EVERYONE'S A CRITIC

This chapter isn't a story. It's a game; a car game to be precise, and a game that I invented. In my line of work, you spend a lot of time sitting in cars and vans with friends on long drives. Since its creation I've played this game with many people, in many countries, on many a long drive. It's something I'm very proud of; perhaps one of my greatest creations. Each time that I've played I've honed in on the rules and playability of the game and now I'm in a position where I'd like to share it with the world. I tried to think of ways to make the game more accessible: could I turn it into a podcast? Or a board game? Or a TV show? But none of them would work, because the best part of the game is its simplicity. You don't need anything to play it apart from three or more people that are up for it and a means of keeping score, be that a pen and paper or a phone. The other thing you need is time. People thinking might not make for exciting TV, but it can help the hours fly by and it can make for a cracking drive. So without further ado, ladies and gentlemen may I present to you… EVERYONE'S A CRITIC

WHAT YOU NEED TO PLAY:
Three or more people
A pen and paper
An opinion

HOW TO PLAY:

The game starts with the driver. They are player 1.

Player 1 must choose a band or musical act that they love that begins with the letter A.

Once they have said their choice out loud, it moves to player 2 in a clockwise direction around the car.

Player 2 must also come up with a band or musical act that begins with the letter A. Ideally one that they think is better than player 1's choice.

Once they have said the band name out loud, it turns to player 3. Player 3 is now the Judge, and it's up to them to decide which band is better.

They can either: MAKE A CALL straight away and award one point to the player who has chosen the best band (in the Judge's opinion), or they can say JUSTIFY.

If they call JUSTIFY, it goes back to player 1, who then has to explain to the Judge why they think their band is the best band, however they see fit. Once they've said their piece, Player 2 then has their chance to convince the Judge. Once the Judge has heard both justifications, they then make a judgement and awards the point to the band they think are the best. Unless someone uses a BUZZER.

Once the point has been awarded, the game moves along in a clockwise motion and travels through the alphabet. So it now starts with Player 2, who has the letter B. They choose their band and say the name out loud, then Player 3 also chooses someone from the letter B and now Player 1 is the Judge.

(This is based on three people playing; if more people are playing, it moves in the same direction, with three players playing each letter. If it's not your go, you can still use a BUZZER.)

You circle through the alphabet until you get to Z. Then you total up the points, and the person with the most points wins.

THE BUZZER:

Each Player has just 2 buzzers to use throughout the game. You can use a buzzer if you're the Judge (3 person game), or it's not your go (4 +). Once both players have said their band name out loud, and before the Judge has made a call or asked for justification, you shout "BUZZER". You then get to choose a band of the current letter. In order to win the point, everyone playing the quiz must unanimously agree that your band is better, without any kind of justification.

THE RULES:

The Judge is always right. If you disagree with the Judge, tough luck; you'll get your chance to be the Judge soon enough, and when you do, you'll be right. If any petty arguments arise (and they will), it's down to whoever is the Judge at that time to make a call. Whatever they say goes.

Don't say any band names out loud for the entirety of the game, unless it's your go and you've made your decision. If you do, you get deducted one point. Whether it's your go, whether you're the Judge, whatever. Even if the letter has already passed, if you mention a band, you lose a point.

THE is invisible, so The Beatles would be classed as a B. And performers go by the first letter of the first name, so Bob Dylan, would also be a B. (You can no longer use either The Beatles

or Bob Dylan in your game, as I've had to use them as an example, but fear not, there's loads of great B's out there).

Take as long as it takes. You can't pass, skip a go or any of that nonsense. Everyone has to wait until you've chosen, or the game can't continue.

Don't cheat. I'd like to think this goes without saying. Because what's the point? Don't look up bands on your phone, or scan through your Spotify library; you're playing this for fun, and cheating will take all the fun out of it. Even if you win, you'll still be a loser.

Have fun.

NO SUCH THING AS A FREE BREAKFAST

"I really enjoyed your gig, but it made me sad," a beautiful girl with sad eyes said to me. She carried on talking after that hard-hitting opening sentence, but I couldn't hear a word she was saying over the old-skool jungle music. She talked for quite some time, and when I saw that she'd stopped, I raised my hands in a confused gesture and shouted over the music, "I didn't hear a word of that!" Then I used my right finger to push my right ear lobe into my ear (an old-skool trick for listening to a conversation in a loud place), faced the ear towards her and gestured for her to repeat whatever she had just said, even if I wasn't sure that I wanted to hear it. "I really enjoyed your gig, but it made me sad," she said again. I braced myself as she explained why.

We were at Lounge On The Farm Festival in Kent. Early July 2011. It was late Sunday night, so late that it was actually Monday morning, I reckon about 3am. The whole festival had shut down, and the last place playing music was a small bar tucked away at the back of the festival. The tent was full of people having a banging time, and the jungle tunes were precisely the right music for the mood of the crowd. I stood in the limbo area between dancefloor and not-dancefloor, not really dancing and not really standing still. Just swaying, smiling and taking it all in, still buzzing off the pills I'd taken earlier that night. I'd played two shows that day, one on the main stage and one in the Groovy Movie Solar Powered Cinema - a legendary festival venue with a name that explains what it does, so I won't bother. The gig in the cinema is the one the girl was referring to, and it was a gig that wasn't even supposed to be a gig. It was supposed to be the premier of my first-ever documentary, a road movie called *The Meaning of Life.*

The first-ever Beans on Toast headline UK tour had been earlier that year. I'd done a fair few tours as a support act and played London hundreds of times, but hadn't done a proper run of headline shows. I didn't have a booking agent, manager or anything like that, but wanted to pull something together, so I put a post out on Facebook saying that I'd play anywhere in the country for £50, food, drink and somewhere to sleep. I can only presume it was a success, based on the fact I've been touring ever since. It was the cementing of a beautiful relationship with the road. It was also the beginning of a beautiful friendship between myself and Bobby Banjo, as it was the first tour we did together (in his car, Brian, RIP), but it certainly wasn't the last. The tour was a riot, and if you'd like to know more about it, you can watch the documentary *The Meaning of Life* because I filmed the whole tour. I stuck a camera in the face of everyone I met along the way and asked them, "What's the meaning of life?" then cut together people's answers with footage of Bob and me zig-zagging all over the country, playing and singing for food and board. It turns out everybody has a different idea as to what the meaning of life is. I was pretty happy with people's answers, and I was pretty happy with the film itself. I wanted to hype up the release, so I looked into places to screen it. I knew they had a cinema at Lounge On The Farm, and I had a good friend who worked at the festival, and so it was arranged. Lounge On The Farm holds a very special place in my heart. It's where I met Lizzy Bee, the love of my life. That was the year before, in 2010.

The festival season of 2010 was a mental one, even by my standards. I'd been getting more and more festival bookings each year, and I'd also picked up a job working for a music charity called Strummerville, an incredible charity set up by Joe Strummer's friends and family after his untimely death. The idea of the charity was to help out young musicians. It had a board of directors, who were either good friends of Joe and themselves successful in music or the arts, or people whom Joe had worked with over the years, or who had made money from The Clash or Joe's solo outings. The board members put in money and worthy goods, and the charity would hand them out to people who couldn't have ever afforded them. It was lovely. My job description was to 'do what Joe would have wanted' and 'keep the fire burning'. Fantastic job descriptions, for a fantastic job, I'm sure you'll agree. I was employed by a magic and powerful woman named Trish, who ran the charity at the time, and we became great friends. I became Robin to her Batman, and while we were working there, we did some wonderful things with the charity. We put on gigs all over the world, provided free rehearsal spaces in West London and Camden, we had a van that could be lent out to bands free of charge for gigs and tours, and Trish would meet with any musician or band that got in touch and dish out priceless industry advice from her years of experience. Good vibes all around.

The core of Strummerville, though, was its Glastonbury campfire - a tradition of Joe's that was turned into an official Glasto area after he'd passed. Family and friends kept the fire burning in his honour year after year, and the charity took over the organisational side things. The fire was wild. I mean, the fire itself was fucking huge and, of course, wild. What sort of fire isn't? But the vibe was also wild. Joe, it seems, was never afraid of a good time, and neither were the crew that had formed in his absence. 'Crew' is the perfect word for the friends I made through Strummerville, and it was a crew that I was happy to be part of. It was at the Glasto campfire that I'd met Trish and that, in turn, had led to me getting the job. After a few years working with the charity, we made the call to take the fire on the road. The idea was to create an area very similar to the Glasto pitch, with a massive fire, sofas, late nights and open minds, and take it around UK festivals. At the same time, we'd take a stage and book shows for all the bands we were working with as a charity, many of whom were struggling to get festival bookings. It was a no-brainer for most promoters. Who wouldn't want an authentic piece of the Joe Strummer legacy at their festival? Everybody wanted us to come. The problem, however, was not many people wanted the campfire because of licensing restrictions. But without the campfire, we were nothing. It's a shame that fire and festivals have become so disconnected. It used to be standard. Anyone who wanted a fire could and would have them in the campsites at all festivals. The fact that this seems so foreign now goes a long way to explaining the world's problems, I would suggest. We only signed up to festivals that weren't scared of a big fire, so that summer, we went to Endorse It In Dorset, Secret Garden Party and Lounge On The Farm.

My role at the festivals was mainly setting up and taking down. During the festival, I would be on hand to fetch firewood, help get a band set up and whatnot, but it wasn't like I had to be anywhere at any particular time. It was very relaxed, as it always was with Strummerville. Which was good because it meant I could go and watch the bands I wanted to see, and at Lounge On The Farm in 2010, Toots And The Maytals were playing: the greatest living reggae band on the planet.

I met Lizzy through mutual friends, Mel and Holly, who ran a beautiful vintage clothes stall called BumbleHogg. Lizzy was working with them at Lounge, doing face-painting. I met up with them on my way to go and watch Toots.

Lizzy and I didn't talk much that night. We danced. And we remembered each other. Eight years later, '54-56' by Toots And The Maytals was the first dance at our wedding.

The next time I saw her after Lounge was New Year's Day. She came to the pub I was running at the time, The Wheelbarrow on Camden High Street. We had David Rodigan playing a set. Yes, you heard me correctly: New Year's Day, not New Year's Eve; and yes, you also heard me correctly: the living legend and one-of-a-kind reggae selector superhero David Rodigan, who was no doubt playing some massive club on New Year's Eve, was coming to play our 200 capacity pub the following night. Ivor, who I worked with at The Wheelbarrow, had sorted the whole thing. It was by far the best event we put on at that place. I started the night behind the bar as it was so busy. I was serving folks as fast as I could, and shortly after I'd started, I turned to the next customer with the standard "What can I get you?" and there she was. Lizzy Bee. My true love, there to complete me, to show me the meaning of life, the beautiful, the confident, the wise, the sexy. The person I would fall for more than I'd ever know possible. My wife. The mother of my child. The love of my life. Lizzy Bee. And she said, "Two pints of cider, please."

That was the night that we got together. We danced, this time to Rodigan, and you can bet your bottom dollar that he spun a bit of Toots. We drank, and we got high. And when the party was finished, we stayed for a lock-in, and when the lock-in was finished, Lizzy and I stayed in the pub. I lived upstairs, but we stayed downstairs, now selecting the tunes ourselves, still dancing. I had a great urge to play her every song I'd ever loved - an urge I'd never had before. We did share a bed that night, and we lay in it without laying one finger on each other. Nothing. At the time, I was living fast, I was sleeping around a fair bit, and a one night stand was a pretty standard procedure. This wasn't that. I knew it straight away. This was something altogether different, something precious, that made me nervous and excited. Patience would be needed. We talked though, non-stop, until morning, then Lizzy stayed for the whole next day, and we talked, lay in bed, and started telling each other about our lives, our hopes and dreams, and this conversation has never stopped. When Lizzy left the following evening, I had to hold back from telling her that I loved her. It was almost difficult to stop the words from falling out of my mouth, but I managed to keep them in.

The next time we saw each other, maybe a week later, we went for a night out, just the two of us. We ended up at a circus squat in the West End of London, on Shaftesbury Avenue, right opposite The Palace Theatre, where *Priscilla, Queen of the Desert* was showing. The squat was a fascinating building, once a Walkabout Australian sports bar. Before that, it had been run by Peter Stringfellow, and had been a celeb hotspot in the '80s and '90s. It was built long before that though, in 1754, as a church. It was a vast building, with hidden rooms, secret tunnels and viewing balconies. I know this because the two of us explored the whole building. It was now in the loose control of a circus community who'd squatted the building with the hope of turning it into a giant community arts space. There was poetry, fire breathing, homemade art galleries and an intriguing mix of intriguing people from all walks of life. Lizzy and I chased each other around the building, catching a bit of music and performance here and there, mainly focused on each other until we ended on the roof of the building. Where we kissed.

It was on. I was in love, and it didn't take long for me to start writing songs about it.

The songs came naturally. As they say, I wanted to 'shout it from the rooftops'. I wanted everyone to know, so they felt good too. Share the love, as they say. It's not like, 'hey, look at me', but more like, 'this exists, and it makes sense'. Singing songs about love seemed to me a generous thing to do. It's what I had to give back. I wrote so many songs about her that six months later, at Lounge On The Farm, I played a whole set of songs about her. By this time, we were head over heels in love. Since that night out and that rooftop kiss, we'd spent more nights together than not, we'd met each other's friends and families, and everyone had got on. Falling in love was easy. I closed my eyes, put my arms out wide and jumped on in.

Young love. What a beautiful thing, and young love on Ecstasy? That can be mind-blowing. I'd done my gig on the main stage at Lounge On The Farm, and as night fell, dropped a pill. My only commitment left at the Festival was watching the film I'd made (with Lizzy's help) in the Groovy Movie Solar Powered Cinema. Not that we planned to watch the film (I'd edited the thing and seen it hundreds of times), but we would be there for the screening.

However, on arrival, it seemed there were problems afoot - something wrong with the file that I'd sent through to Jerry, who ran the tent. My fault, it seemed, but it also seemed there was no way of screening my film. Disaster. But not for someone loved up on real (and artificial) love. I took the problem in my stride and did whatever I do when disaster strikes. I went and got my guitar. No film, no problem, we'd do a gig instead.

By the time I got back, I was properly buzzing. Playing high was nothing new for me. Far from it (one day, I'll tell you the Damien Rice / Latitude story), but there was something about the mood I was in: soppy, romantic, deep, and loved up. It was dark, warm and welcoming in the tent, and everyone was sat on the floor. I perched on the edge of the small stage in front of the blank projector screen. There wasn't much room left in the tent, so Lizzy sat on stage next to me.

The minute I started the set, the crowd, the tent, the festival and the world disappeared. It was just Lizzy and me. In love. True Love. I told her so, and I sang the songs I'd written for her, and I talked about how lucky I was to find her and how I'd now do whatever I had to do to keep her, to make her happy, for this feeling to continue. As I wrapped up all my new love songs, slowly, the crowd and the world at large reappeared around us, and we got a round of applause. Then we ducked out of the tent, held hands and walked off into the festival night, looking for music that would make us dance. I remember being pleased with how the set had gone, unlike any gig I'd played before, really honest and fucking deep, and the right time and place for an emotional set like that. Personally, I was pretty happy with the show. Until I met the girl with the sad eyes.

With my finger now plunged into my lughole, I could hear what she had to say over the banging jungle. She was in the cinema tent and loved the new songs, but she said that they made her sad. They made her feel lonely. Why didn't she have someone like that to write songs about? Or someone to write songs about her? Or even to think and feel that way about each other? I was really high, and it was really loud, so my response was, "Stop looking, start finding!" Even though this is a motto I'm generally fond of, it wasn't the right moment for it at all. It made the girl look even sadder. I changed my approach. "Let's find you love in this tent right now. Look around, loads of interesting and up-for-it looking people in here. If you had to fall in love with anyone in this tent, who would it be?" Before she could reply, I said, "Don't think, just point." She didn't deliberate. She just pointed at a chap on the other side of the dancefloor, also standing in the limbo segment. I didn't say anything else to the girl. I just walked up to the guy she'd pointed at and said, loudly over the music, "My mate over there fancies you, you should go over and talk to her."

Fucking obvious, I know, corny even, but classic too; at least he knew what I was on about. He smiled and nodded, and I walked off in the other direction, making an Irish exit. I'd had my fill of jungle, I needed to find Lizzy, and then we needed to find our tent. Plus, this girl's confession had got my brain a whirring. It was only a brief exchange, in the early hours of the morning, on a dancefloor, but it raised a whole bunch of questions about me, my songs and why I sing them.

I guess it's a question of tone, and finding the right tone in my artistic and creative endeavours. I'm trying to be honest in my songwriting, and to find some truth in who I am. I'm not trying to tell other people what to do or how to think. I'm just trying to get across how I feel, and the truth is I'm more truthful in my songs than I am in my life. My songs know me better than I do. I can explain myself, both in songwriting and under the lights of a stage, easier than anywhere else. This is true for those of my songs that could be labelled political, and is definitely true for my love songs. I am a loving husband to Lizzy, and I tell her and show her how I feel daily, but it's much easier for me to express my deepest feelings towards her in song than in any other way. I think if I rolled out some of the lines from my songs in bed, I'd get laughed out of it. It's for that exact reason that art exists; it exists to say the things we wish we could say, to say the things we didn't even know we wanted to say. And I'm not talking about my songs now; I'm talking about art and creativity in general. It's so fucking important. The world needs it, and we need it. We're not just bystanders or spectators. For life to survive and give our lives meaning, we all must strive to be creative, if not in song, then in dance, and if not in dance, then in cooking, in the way we dress, or how we talk. Art is everything, and it has everything we need to set us free. In moments of true inspiration, the walls crumble down. You reveal your true self to yourself and those around you. I thought that's what I was doing the night before in the Groovy Movie Solar Powered Cinema, having a moment of truly free expression and sharing my love with the world, or at least the tent, even though I had no idea they were there at the time. Still, it turns out it made someone sad. That wasn't the plan.

This sort of shit went round and round my head all night. I couldn't sleep, though that was probably as much the E as the existential crisis, or the minor mental breakthrough I had about the meaning of art (which happened to be the name of my second documentary). Lizzy slept, and I thought it out, over and over and round and round, until the sun completed its lap and rose, bright and early, hot and horny to the east of our tent. The heat in the tent got unbearable, Lizzy slept on regardless, so I slipped out to get us some breakfast.

I was still thinking about tone, about art, about sadness and love as I joined the back of a queue for a double-decker bus that said 'The Breakfast Club' on the side and was selling pricey eggs rolls and cups of tea. As usual, the morning after a big night, I wasn't feeling sociable. I kept my hands in my pockets and my head down, thinking and thinking until I arrived at the front of the queue. I looked up as a voice said, "What can I get you?"

It was her, the girl, with the sad eyes. But her eyes weren't sad anymore. They were alive, on fire. "It's you!" She said to me, beaming.

"You can have your breakfast for free."

BEAUTIFUL ALICE

I've told the stories in this book many times to many different people. But not this one. This story is different. I have, in the past, told it to a few people very close to me when the mood was right, and it was more like I was confiding in them than banging on about one of my escapades, like I usually do. It's different for a few reasons. Firstly, the story is unbelievable, and I mean that in the literal sense, as in you won't believe that it's true, which is fair enough. If someone told it to me, I'm not sure how I'd feel about it. All I know is what I believe, and that's what I will share. It also blows some huge questions wide open, but we're not going to be asking the big questions here. I'll just tell you how it went down.

I've chosen not to share this story before because it affects the lives and emotions of people I don't really know; it affects them deeply, and the story is based around a tragic accident. If you're now reading this, it means that this story has been read and approved by the people I'm about to talk about, and I have their permission to share my story with you. They are Alice's wonderful family, who originally got in contact with me. The story starts with an email:

---------- Forwarded message ---------
From: Beautiful Alice <beautifulalice11@gmail.com>
Date: Fri, Jan 22, 2016 at 11:10 AM
Subject: Beautiful Alice gig
To: <beansontoastmail@gmail.com>

There are two ways of spreading light: To be the candle or the mirror that reflects it…

Dear Jay,

This is our story...

Tragically, at the end of 2014, our Beautiful Alice (19) - and her wonderful friend Summer (21) – were cruelly taken from us in a terrible accident that could, and should, have been prevented. They were coming home to us in just 4 days, having spent the previous 10 weeks volunteering, through VSO, in an impoverished township in South Africa. We are fighting to prevent such accidents from happening again. Our loss is unbearable, but we are trying to find the courage to keep going. One of the ways we are doing this is by raising money to support some of the projects that Alice was involved within her short - but wonderful - life.

Alice worked on several projects supporting local, needy communities in both South Africa and Cambodia. Alice loved music, dancing and sunshine. She described her favourite festival – The Secret Garden Party – as 'a little piece of heaven on earth'. We have organised our own festival to honour Alice and all that she stood for. Following the huge success of our event last year, we are proud to be hosting Beautiful Alice Festival 2016 – Charity Jam, on June 4th in St Albans, Herts.

The event is being held on a private field, and we are hoping for around 1000 people to join us to celebrate Alice's colourful life in a way that would make Alice proud.

All profits will go to support charities that Alice believed in – including the school in Cambodia, The FKC, who we are actively working with and where we have already been able to provide funding for a whole new classroom, essential repairs and maintenance to existing buildings, supplies and a clean water well.

We already have offers of help and expert assistance pouring in, but we are writing to you in the hope that you might consider joining us and make our day complete. You always made Alice so happy - your music is a mirror to her sense of humanity, compassion and injustice - and especially to her wonderful, beautiful, powerful spirit.

If you're unable to come, perhaps you would consider sending a message of support - either written or by video, that we can share prior to the event on our website and during the day on a large screen on our main stage.

Please help us to continue to keep Alice's light shining brightly, and do get in touch if you would like any further information.

With love from us all,

Alice's mum - Suzie, and Alice's cousins – Joe and Adam x

Over the years, I've played many charity festivals and events, some deeply personal to those involved. I've also had many invites to play charity gigs that I've not been able to play; my summers generally get booked up quite quickly. Something about this email though, the tragedy, the strength and the love in the words, really hit me. Luckily, I didn't have a show booked in on that day, so I could take the gig.

After it was confirmed and in the diary, I kind of forgot about the email. I read it for the second time on 4th June on the train to St Albans to play the show.

On arrival at the festival, the first person I saw was Suzi, who came over to introduce herself as Alice's mum. A kind-hearted and strong woman, putting a brave face on for what was clearly a very sad and painful day for her. We ended up sitting down and talking for a bit; I tried my best to offer my condolences and asked her about Alice. She explained that Alice used to come to watch me play at Secret Garden Party every year and listen to my music all the time, and that it meant a lot to everyone that I could come and play today, including Alice.

The conversation hit me hard, not that I let on in front of Suzi, of course. It turns out I, too, was now putting on a brave face. Again, it's the thing about putting your music and your heart out in the open. If people you've never met feel like they know you and are, in fact, friends, then it hurts when something happens to that friend. And the loss of someone so young, so unnecessary, was heartbreaking. Suzi had said that they were honoured to have me. Now I felt honoured to be there, honoured to be part of this story, as sad as it was. And if I can do a tiny little bit to celebrate the short life of this beautiful soul, then I would. I got a drink and walked around the small, colourful and heartfelt festival, thinking about the songs I'd play later that afternoon.

My gig was in a stretch tent, a good size for the amount of people at the festival. It was a sunny day, and I knew a gig in the shade would be a welcome one. I arrived with plenty of time to spare. It seemed there wasn't an act before me. In fact, when I got to the tent, it was empty save for three kids who were playing, running all over the tent and the stage. There was a bit too much seating in the tent for my liking. With smaller festivals and gigs, it's always worth setting up the tent or room appropriately. I knew the show would be better if we moved the seating to the edge so that people could sit on the floor and more people could see the stage, as the stage was the same level as the floor. I roped the kids in to help, which they were more than happy to do. It turned out they were in the tent waiting for my show.

I soundchecked, the tent filled up, and I started my set. As I'd hoped, people were sitting on the floor and standing around the edges. I could see Suzi and a few of Alice's friends who I'd been chatting to that afternoon in the crowd. After I'd played my first song, a young girl, she must have been, at a guess, six years old, stood up at the very front of the seated crowd and began to stare right at me. She was looking me dead in the eye - an intense, electric stare, without flinching, and giving her full undivided attention. I played another song, feeling as though I was playing to this young child who was still on her feet, still staring right at me, with no real emotion visible on her face, certainly not one that was easy to read. Now, this would typically be quite an uncomfortable thing. Of course, people look at you when you're on stage. That's half the point, but a kid that young with a stare that intense, standing right up at the front of the tent when everyone else was sitting - it's not a typical thing to expect. But it wasn't uncomfortable at all. Not for me, not for anyone else in the crowd, and not for this girl who was staring. It felt natural, almost like a spell had been cast over the tent. This intense look and this quite abstract behaviour lasted for most of my set. I didn't comment on it, which is unlike me. I was completely at ease with it - more than at ease. I was concerned all day about finding the right tone for the show: a celebration, but a tragedy. I was unsure of the words to say or the songs to sing, but all that faded once I'd started the gig. The words and the songs came easy, the gig flew by, and towards the end, the girl with the electric eyes sat back down.

Even after the show, nobody, including myself, talked about the girl's behaviour, not until I was leaving the festival a few hours later, when I saw the girl with her mum, and so I walked over. The girl had completely changed. Now she was nervous, clinging to her mum's leg. She didn't want to talk or even look at me. I felt like I needed to go over to say hi, but now I was embarrassed about it. I smiled at her mum, who said she'd never seen her daughter act that way before, ever. It was very unlike her, she said, and she'd never even seen her stand that still for so long, she was usually so nervous. "It was almost like she was someone else," she told me. Again I tried to say hi to the girl, who was having none of it, and again I became very embarrassed. So I quickly said my goodbyes and went on my way.

It's not very often that I sleep in my own bed after a festival show, but St Albans is a tiny little train ride from London, and I was back in my flat before sunset. Lizzy was away for the weekend. I'd picked up a bottle of wine on the way back and was intending on having an evening alone with my thoughts and my guitar.

That night, half the bottle gone, I was thinking about Alice, about the life snatched away and how it had affected all those around her, all those she loved and all those who loved her. I've been lucky enough to live a life without being too close to death. My time will come as it will for all those I love, but I've been fortunate, and as of yet, I've never lost anyone extremely close to me, save my grandparents, who all bowed out gracefully after good innings. I was lucky. I knew it. I started to think back to the gig, and then an image of the girl with the electric eyes popped into my head, and a feeling came rushing over me. Like a crack of lightning, I had a realisation. It flooded me like an epiphany, a switch being flicked. Instantly I knew it to be true, as I still know it to be true now. That girl, the one standing up, that was Alice. She'd come to watch the gig. How? I didn't ask and care not to know, but it was her eyes that were shining up at me on the stage, not the eyes of a nervous six-year-old, but the eyes of Alice. With her came the spell, the feeling of comfort that came over the tent that made everyone feel at ease. All of a sudden it seemed clear, seemed obvious, seemed right. It still gives me goosebumps to think about it and write it up now.

As I said, I don't expect you to believe me. It's just how I feel. Weirdly, it hasn't made me overthink about what happens when we die or any of those huge, unanswerable questions. It was just like the fabric of the world was torn for a slight moment, and I happened to catch it in the corner of my eye. I wrote a song that was kind of about it, but I didn't talk to anyone about my epiphany, not for a long time anyway. Now it's a distant memory, but a beautiful one. This one's for you, Alice.

ART

This story begins in Poundland on Camden High street in 2011 - an excellent place for the story to start, because although this is a story about art, this is also a story about money. It seems the two are always connected, whether we want them to be or not. Now, talking about money is never easy, is it? It has a strange way about it, brings out the worst in people. I don't believe it makes the world go around, but it is important to know its worth. I'm worried that this story, about money, might come off as bragging, as it has a happy ending. I promise that's not the case. I'm very proud of the tale I'm about to tell, but if there's a meaning in here anywhere, it's in the art, not the money.

I would like to be straight up and tell you the whole truth here, and for you to understand this story, I have to go into its finances, the actual figures. I'll go into detail, but only because it's what makes the story. If you've got this far, to the last chapter of my second book, I'd like to think I can talk to you like a close friend, that I can confide in you personal details of my life - that's what I do in my songs, anyhow. Hopefully, you'll be happy for me and for the fact that this book has a happy ending, because it is the story of how I bought a house. With art.

It may start back in Poundland, but it ends right here, today, in real-time. This story will bring us right up to this moment, me sitting at my desk writing the last chapter in January 2021. I promised at the start of this book, which I started nine months ago, that it wasn't going to be a book about the pandemic, and it hasn't been. This chapter though, which finishes in the last five months of my life, going through the most mental time in recent human history, will have to touch on that, but purely as a backdrop.

I despise Poundland. I have no idea why I was in there on that fateful day. At the time, both Lizzy and I were living above The Wheelbarrow on Camden High Street. I got the room in exchange for the work I was doing promoting shows in the pub and pulling the odd pint, so we weren't paying rent in the traditional sense. About six of us lived upstairs at any given time. I could see Poundland from my bedroom window, and I avoided it at all costs. There must have been a reason for me to go in. It escapes me now, but there I was, and I found myself looking at a blank canvas; a plain white, stretched canvas, 8 x 10 inches, and it cost, as you can imagine, £1.

The endless possibility of a blank canvas is surely one of the fires that keep the human heart burning. The words 'blank canvas' are used as an analogy the world over, for lives about to be lived and the fate and mystery that lies ahead. All paintings start blank. All the beautiful paintings that have shaped the world in which we live, paintings that reduce people to tears, paintings that start wars, paintings that sell for millions, paintings of madness, culture, religion, sex, love, life and death. They all started out as blank as the canvas in Poundland.

Personally, I set my sites a bit lower. "If you can put something on that canvas and make it worth £2, then you've doubled your money," I thought to myself. Not immediately thinking of an idea, I didn't buy a blank canvas, but I kept it in mind.

A few months later, I was at a party at Flaxon Ptootch. A hairdresser-art gallery-legendary community fixture on Kentish

Town High Street, run by an extraordinary fellow called Michael. Once a month they change the art and throw a party. The hairdressing stuff is tucked away, and out pops a good sound-system playing good music, a sneaky little bar banging out strong but affordable cocktails, a picturesque garden out back and art fucking everywhere. It's ramshackle in the best way possible, and always full of interesting people who are up to something. Michael holds court over proceedings and does whatever is needed to encourage people to buy the art. After the party, the art stays on the walls and is on sale for a month, until it changes at the next shindig. A neat set up, and back when I lived in Camden and Kentish Town, I found myself there a lot.

I was standing looking at a new piece of art on the wall. I was pissed. I turned to the guy standing next to me and said:

"It's shit."

Which is a pretty shitty thing to say. Levi, whom I knew from a few previous visits, said:

"Why?"

I mean, it was fine. There was nothing wrong with the painting. It was just a bit naff. It didn't really say anything or do anything to me, but there, in this gallery setting, it seemed to be asking my opinion, and my opinion was, it was shit. So I said it out loud. As I said, I was drunk. Levi, who knows what's going on and is no fool, said:

"Well, I'd rather be an artist who paints a shit picture that hangs in a gallery than to be the drunk idiot who comes along and calls it shit."

He was, of course, right. I regretted saying it. But then he said:

"Think you could do better?"

I'm not sure if he meant, do I think I could make better art, or if I could do better in my life and stop saying stupid shit. I answered, "I'm going to try," to both questions.

Later that night, I thought back to that Poundland canvas, and an idea struck. Ding! The next day I called Michael and said I wanted to do an art show. As soon as possible. He was reluctant, probably because I didn't have any art to show him, and didn't want to tell him about this big idea I'd had. I talked him around by promising I'd play a gig at the opening and drum up some heads to come down and buy some of the art that I wouldn't tell him about. He agreed, and it was booked in. I had until February to prepare, which was a few months down the line.

My first and only art showing didn't take much preparation. I went back to Poundland, and I bought 100 canvases for £1 each. Then I got a can of spray paint and sprayed big numbers onto the blank canvases: 1 to 100. Nothing else on the canvas but a big black number. Then I went to Flaxon Ptootch with Lizzy Bee and Fun Bobby (Dave Danger's cousin, don't you know), and we hung the canvases in order: 1 to 100. The following night was the art show launch party, and they would be on sale. Number 1 would be £1, number 2 would be £2 and so on and so forth, right up to £100 for the canvas that said 100 - that I'd bought for £1. It was genius. Or at least I thought so.

I was riddled with overconfidence. I was so convinced that people would buy into the idea, and that they would therefore buy the art. I thought it was hilarious, and genuinely had delusions of selling all the pieces on the opening night. Being bad at numbers, I went to my friend Johnny Manning, the mathematical genius, to do the figures for me. He informed me that:

If I sold all the art, I'd make £3,081 profit.

This was after £285 costs and one third of all sales going to the gallery.

In order to break even, I needed to sell numbers 1 - 29.

What could go possibly wrong?

Well, people could not buy them. That could happen - and it did. Michael was quick to inform me, this wasn't even art: just some smartarse poking fun at it. Yes, it's funny, yes people get it, but do they want to part ways with £12 or £67 for one of these? No, it turned out, they didn't. Also, my original plan of it just costing £1 was out the window. As you can see, it had cost a lot more to pull the whole thing off, and I'd racked up nearly £300 in costs. A £2 canvas wasn't doubling the money at all. It's not like I was mad skint at the time, but I didn't have money to burn. I started the project purely for the art, hoping I might have some fun and make some money, not lose it.

People did show up. It was snowing, and it was a weekday, and various other lame excuses I've used over the years for people not showing up to my gigs. But people did show up, and they wanted to see me sing songs, but nobody wanted the art. I got hammered - really hammered, trying to mask my ridicule. I kept waiting for Michael to tell me that people had bought something but by 10pm, we'd sold 4 pieces and made £40. There was nothing to do but take to the stage. Which was essentially the corner of the gallery.

At the end of the gig, I gave all the pieces of art away. Or at least I tried. By this time, even I had given up on calling them art. On stage, I referred to them as "stupid number things" and then proclaimed them free for the taking. The party raged into the night, but come morning, there were still numbers hanging on the wall. I couldn't even give them away. My first art show had been a failure, a flop. But still, I wasn't deterred. The remaining pieces were still on course to hang on the gallery wall for one month. And I'd been filming the past 48 hours.

I went home and made a film about it called *The Meaning of Art.* In the midst of getting hammered, playing the show and giving the art away, I'd also asked as many people as possible the question "What's the meaning of art?" and filmed their response, with a plan to make a follow up to my widely ignored debut film, *The Meaning of Life.* I edited it the following day, and put the film up on Youtube. My plan was for people to see the film and rush to Kentish Town to grab a piece of this inventive and funny art made by a foolhardy folk singer.

Another flop. In the whole month, we didn't sell one more piece of art. It looked a right state on the wall of the hairdressers, with half the numbers gone and the other half haphazardly scattered over the wall. Michael would have taken them down immediately if he could have, but he stuck to his word like a true gentleman. At the end of the month, I went to see Michael. The show had run at a loss, both for him and me. I'd taken on art, and I'd lost, he explained as he gave me a big pile of the unsold canvases. At this point, even I didn't want them - I was on my way out somewhere else, and didn't fancy carting them about all night. When I asked if I could leave them at the gallery, he said I could, but he'd paint them white again and give them to real artists. Woah: the power of a blank canvas. I took them and displayed them on the streets of Kentish Town between the gallery and the Tube station; still trying to call it art. I bang on about not dropping litter all the time, it's my thing. Absolutely avidly never drop any litter and will openly criticise those who do. And there I was, littering the streets with unwanted art. All in the name of art.

Maybe for art, this was a success?

Earth spins around the sun a few times, and then it's 2015, and I'm killing time in Chicago for an afternoon. I was on tour with Frank Turner, and it was everything I dreamed it would be. Big shows and amazing crowds every night for two weeks around the US of A. I had the day to myself to walk around the city. I have no idea why I walked into the art supply shop, but I did. Amongst all the arty-farty-crafty stuff in an enormous central Chicago art store, I saw them again. The little blank canvases. 8 x 10, exactly the same as the Poundland bargains. This time they were $1 each, in a bargain bin, actually making them cheaper than Poundland. I bought every canvas I could carry and headed back to The House of Blues for the gig.

This time around, the idea had formed very quickly, mainly because it was already half in action. For the tour so far, I'd been selling loads of T-shirts at the merch stand, as bands do on tour. At the time, I didn't have the means or the money to print proper T-shirts in the States. So I'd been buying plain white T-shirts and just writing 'Beans on Toast' on them, and I tell you what, people fucking loved them. I'm not sure anyone ever actually wore one, but they were selling like hotcakes. Every day I was heading to some hellhole Walmart to buy cheap, questionably made T-shirts for $1 and selling them for $10. The problem was the T-shirts actually looked rubbish - the pen and the fabric didn't pair up well. But now I had these new canvases, the possibilities were endless. I managed to carry 20 of them back to the gig, and I sold them all that night.

It took me a few gigs to find my feet with them. That first night in Chicago, I drew stick-man-style portraits. I stood at the merch with the pile of canvases, and I sold them for $10 each, but the deal was, you had to pay me before I drew or wrote anything. As I said, I sold out, but the pictures were naff. The following day in Dinkytown, Minnesota, I sniffed out an art supply store and went there immediately after arriving in town. I bought another 20. That night, I changed my tactics. I wrote one word on each canvas and signed the bottom corner 'Beans on Toast'. When people asked how much they were, I replied, "How much have you got?" and said they could pay whatever they liked for them. Some people paid $4. Some people paid $40. They sold out again. The next night in Denver, after another visit to an art supply shop, I made 2 trips and bought 40 blank canvases. That night, with half the canvases, I wrote a few words on them. When people asked how much they were, I said I was holding a silent auction, and if they bid more than the last person, they could have the canvas. People bid high. Whatever they bid, I always gave them the canvas. It was mental. It kept going throughout the tour. People loved them. I sold out night after night, as many as I could carry. The tour was always going to be a success. It was travelling with good friends, singing songs to huge crowds on the other side of the world, it was wonderful. But for me personally, it wasn't going to make money. Without the art, the tour would have run at a loss or maybe broken even, a small musician touring the States. That's just how things are. The system is rigged and all that. But not now, This art and all the bullshit I'd pulled at the merch desk had meant it was also a financial success. I'd be coming home with cash in my pocket.

When you're playing a support slot on the other side of the world and getting your music out to people for the first time, that's the kind of time to pull off this kind of prank, or so I saw it. It had been amazing, but once I was home, I was sure that that would have been the end of it. No way would I get away with it any more than I already had. My first show back was in Glasgow at a place called Stereo. I fucking love Glasgow, a city I'd played many times before, and have some great stories about. I know Glasgow well enough to know that you can't take Glaswegians for fools. Yeah, maybe in America as a support act, it might be funny to charge someone £10 for a word written on a canvas. But in Glasgow? At a headline show of mine? These people had already paid £15 just to come and watch me bang on about whatever I'm banging on about that day. It felt rude to try and sell them at my own shows. But also idiotic not to try.

The canvases had gotten better. At one of my many art supply shop missions, I'd picked up a big fancy pen. Originally I'd started just using sharpies, but once I got this massive oil pen, the style of the canvas had significantly improved. I'd also started to hone in on the words and phrases I was putting on the canvases. My handwriting had improved too. I guess the thing behind the scenes here that helped make it work was that all the artwork for my albums, posters or anything related to Beans on Toast since I'd started this journey was written in my handwriting. With a cute little 'a' that I stole from my mum. Maybe handwriting is a dying art, and that's why people liked them. Combined also with the words: I'd use bold, honest and straightforward words like 'Love', 'Family', 'Peace'. I'd also write lyrics: 'Don't Believe The Bullshit', 'Down the Pub' and so on. I found that people would buy the positive ones quicker. I started writing 'Be Nice' and 'You're my Favourite'. I also wrote 'Expensive Art', letting everyone know that I wasn't taking this all that seriously. That one was always a big seller. I convinced myself it was a worthy idea and that, in fact, I should try it out on the Scottish crowd, and en route to Glasgow, Bobby and I stopped off at a Hobby Craft and filled our boots with 8 x 10 canvases. Not quite as cheap as Poundland, but in Hobby Craft buying packs of 10, each canvas was coming in at about £1.50. I bought 20.

Trying to think of a statement that might resonate with Glasgow and it's fine people, I wrote 'I Fucking Love You' on a canvas. It looked cool. It had something about it. The first person that walked through the door that night came straight to the merch stand and bought the 'I Fucking Love You' canvas. I wrote the same on all the remaining blank canvases. We sold out before the gig had even started.

It was the beginning of something very beautiful. Strong words, in a nice pen on a blank canvas for £10. We stopped at a Hobby Craft every other day of the tour, clearing out shop after shop of 8 x 10 canvases. The tactic was to write up half of them with the new favourite slogans - 'Be Nice', 'I Fucking Love You', 'Don't Believe The Bullshit', and so on - and then leave the other half blank. At the end of the gig, I'd hang out at the merch and write up whatever people wanted on them. Hanging out after a show and signing stuff is always fun, and a great way to meet loads of people who have come along to the gig. But doing this was better than signing a CD or vinyl. It felt like we were creating something together and having a laugh doing it. Everyone loved the canvases. They outsold T-shirts and CDs tenfold.

I've been selling art at my shows ever since, and it always sells more than anything else. That's crazy when you put it into context. It sits next to an album of music that took the time and energy to write, then the skills and the cost of recording it, producing it, turning it into a CD. Making an album costs a fortune, and that album sits on the merch stand for £10 - next to a piece of art. Lizzy had worked some magic. We were buying the canvases in bulk before a tour at 70p each, and they take 30 seconds to make. But they sell for £10. On the other side of the art, you'd find my first book, so many words, around 40,000, so much time and thought and love put into it, then it had to be edited, typeset, printed and bound, and there it sits for £10. The same price as the 30-second art piece. It was beautiful. Of course, I understand that one wouldn't work without the other - that is what was beautiful about it. I'm not knocking writing and releasing albums, far from it, that's why I'm here, and that's what I love, but now the art was helping me do that. As time progressed and the touring continued, the money from the art helped feed my family and pay my rent.

Because alongside this tale of art, a lot had been going on in my life. The Wheelbarrow ran its course a year or so after the original art show, and Lizzy and I had to move out. Knowing that we wanted to live together for the rest of our lives, I figured it was probably time to stop living in big groups above rowdy boozers.

I'd been doing that since I moved into Nambucca, aged 23, and for the following ten years, I'd never actually paid rent as such. I worked, fucking hell, I worked my socks off booking bands, putting on club nights, tours, doing posters, websites, pulling pints, changing barrels, emptying the dishwashers and curating a feel and a vibe for the venues. I enjoyed the work, so it didn't really feel like work (it didn't really pay like work either) but in exchange, I got a roof above my head and booze in my belly. After working this way in three venues in North London, a change was coming. I'd just met Lizzy. I was in love. I was making money, making art and making music, and so we rented a flat.

A beautiful flat it was too. Still haunted by my history, it ended up being above an old pub, but this one had been turned into an Italian Restaurant. It was on Chatsworth Road in East London. It had high ceilings, a double bedroom and an open plan kitchen and living room. We adored it. As much as living above a boozer has its benefits and charms, it also has its downsides. Generally, they are run down, old buildings, or you could say, shit-holes. Perfect for a 20-year-old, but I'd had my fill. Now 32, I was over the moon to have a bit of privacy, a usable kitchen and a place of our own. It was in this flat that I wrote the song 'I'm Home When You Hold Me', and Lizzy and I made a video of ourselves dancing around our little flat and eating nice food from the local Spar. The flat was just around the corner from Homerton Hospital, where, four years later, our daughter was born. We knew we'd need more room if we wanted to raise a human, so we left the flat that she'd been conceived in and moved around the corner to Hackney Wick.

The house in Hackney Wick was perfect. We actually went to view it when Lizzy was pregnant, very soon after we'd found out the news. All sorts of thoughts, feelings, fears and new emotions were running wild in my head. Was I really going to be a dad?

So many questions. Could I do it? How do you do it? It felt a bit like an impossible task. No matter how hard I tried, I couldn't visualise it, I couldn't imagine Lizzy and me with a baby. But the morning we went to view this house, everything fitted together. All of a sudden, I could visualise it, and it looked beautiful. This was where we'd raise our daughter. She would have her own room, we would have a garden, the neighbours had kids. It felt safe. It felt possible. The house wasn't a million miles away from the house I grew up in, it was 2-up-2-down terrace house that looked like it should have been in the Essex suburbs, but it was in Hackney Wick, a creative and super-stylish spot in East London, with nightlife, cafes, art galleries, street art and all the joys of city living on your doorstep. As I said, it was perfect. It was even on a road called Beanacre Close. Clearly, it was meant to be. We were the first people to view the house that morning, and I convinced the landlady not to let anyone else see it that day, running to the bank to get cash to lay down a deposit to secure the place. Which we did.

Talking of cash, I did promise to give you some specifics, didn't I? To back up the story. Well, the first flat in Chatsworth Road was £1,400 a month, before bills and council tax, so all in it was around £1,600. At the time, I was touring and gigging a lot, playing lots of festivals and releasing my music through Xtra Mile Recordings. I was also booking bands and promoting a venue in Camden called The Monarch, bringing in some cash. The rent was obviously expensive, it was London after all, but between Lizzy and I, we could afford it, and personally, I didn't really have anything to compare it to, so I went along with it.

The house in Hackney Wick was slightly more at £1,500 a month, but we were getting so much more for it. I knew, however, that something would need to change. As it was, I didn't have a spare minute in the day. I'd been non-stop pretty much my whole life. It's how I've always operated, and at that moment, between The Monarch and the gigs and the writing and releasing music, I had absolutely no time to spare, which had been fine until that point, but now I had a baby to think about. I needed to have time to raise a child, but also needed to be able to pay the rent.

There was no way I would stop making music, so I had to pull away from my role at The Monarch, but I now needed my music alone to support me - something I'd never asked of it before. Not just me either, it had to support my family. Lizzy had started to take control of my merch sales. It happened naturally. I was doing a shoddy job when we met, and Lizzy, in her infinite wisdom, understands the world of retail and online sales. Until this point, I'd only sold merch at gigs, never through my website, so she set about changing that. We roped my mum and dad in to help with posting the merch out - a proper little cottage industry. It worked well. This was also the time my first book came out. Lizzy knows the book world, and together, we self-published and distributed it using the systems that we had in place for the merch. The book sold way better than I could have imagined, and the distribution network was a dream, mum and dad sending everything out and replying to concerned people on email and Lizzy running the shop. It worked so well in fact that I made the decision to leave Xtra Mile Recordings and start to release my own music. Not because I don't love them - I do, and I had them to thank for getting me to where I was - but after releasing nine albums, I felt I had it in me to release an album off my own back, with my family's help, of course. It worked.

Rent was paid, money was saved. I was still gigging, writing and releasing music, but I now also had time to hang out with Wren, our daughter, who was born in 2018. I had three months with a clear diary when she was born, no work commitments at all, the most beautiful time of my life, and I knew that there aren't many jobs or professions in this world that allow for a parent to have three months' paternity leave. But I'd managed it. We were happy, we had our house, we had each other, and the years went rolling by.

When I said our house in Beanacre was perfect, there was obviously one big matter that wasn't perfect, and that was the fact that it wasn't our house. We were, of course, renting it. After a few days, it felt like our house, and once we'd been there a few years, it felt like a home, where we could stay for eternity. As we watched Wren grow and made memories together between those four walls, we often talked about 'buying a place', but the whole prospect was fucking depressing. A house two doors down from ours went on sale for £500,000 - half a million quid! Yes, I loved the house that I was pretending was mine, but how on earth could it be worth such an incredible amount of money? Surely If you had that sort of money, you'd buy an island, not a two bedroom house. Fair enough, we were in the beating heart of gentrified London. We knew it was a sought-after area in a sought-after city, but still; it felt utterly unrealistic. Looking at Rightmove just added to the depression. Any half-decent flat in London was about the same. Now we'd had a garden and a two bedroom house, we couldn't justify moving to a small flat without a garden just so we could own the building, or get on some property ladder - that wouldn't be fair to Wren. Many of our friends started to buy houses, moving further out east to Leyton and Forest Gate, but still paying around £450,000 - the kind of money we knew we couldn't afford.

Yes, we'd been saving. But we didn't have anywhere near what we'd need for a deposit, and I had no idea what my credit score would even be like. It's a conversation I'd been dodging for many years. Personally, I'd never had a credit card; I couldn't justify spending money I didn't have, and I didn't want to live a life in debt. I always avoided them like the plague, something you think would work in your favour if you're trying for a mortgage, but it turns out the opposite is true. If you've not borrowed money in the past, banks see that as suspicious, and tend not to want to lend you money. People had warned me of this over the years. So every time we started talking about buying a place, we came to the same conclusion: we couldn't do it. And we certainly couldn't afford to do it in London, the city we called home. What was even more frustrating was knowing that if we somehow managed to get a mortgage, then our monthly payments would go down. Renting is way more expensive, which makes no sense whatsoever, and the fact that we'd paid our expensive rent every month without fail for four years would hold no sway on the bank - they didn't care about that, at all. Frustrating, yes, but hardly surprising, the system is rigged and all that. So be it, we didn't let it get us down. We rented our house, and we lived our lives.

That brings us right up to last year, the dreaded 2020. The year actually started out alright. On 31st January, I kicked off my biggest headline run to date. Ticket sales had gone up since the last few tours, shows were selling out, the venues were bigger, and the shows were wild. I was doing what I loved and getting paid for it. And the art? Fuck me, it was still flying out. More people at the shows basically meant more people buying canvases. The tour was by far the highest-earning tour I'd ever done; we wrapped up with a sold-out show at The Tufnell Park Dome, and I came home with money in the bank, real money.

I had a big year planned too. I was setting back off on tour in the UK in April, and had festival bookings all summer, a European tour in the autumn, and had already confirmed another headline outing for the winter. It felt exciting. But, of course, none of that happened.

We'd heard rumours of the Coronavirus while on tour. It felt like a distant thing, another thing that had the media's attention that would pass without affecting me or anyone I knew personally, like so many things before it in this hyper-connected, news-addicted era. It started to feel a bit more real once I'd got back from the road, and by the time of my next gig, shit had hit the fan. I played a show at MK11 in Milton Keynes on 14th March, and everyone was in panic mode. I was in talks with the venue all day about if it should even go ahead or not. Nobody knew what to do or how to react to the news of a new infectious virus spreading rapidly around the world. The show did go ahead, but I had the feeling it might be my last show for a while. And I was right. Over the next few months, gigs got cancelled, rescheduled, pushed back and pushed back, and one by one, the festivals dropped off.

As the country went into lockdown, Lizzy and I started to get chesty coughs, me slightly, Lizzy more so, and she was running a temperature. Then Wren's temperature went through the roof and stayed there. We were in a position where, any other day, we would have gone straight to the hospital, but all advice was to stay away from hospitals, take paracetamol, and ride it out, and so we did. It was terrifying. I did what I always do when disaster strikes, and I picked up my guitar. In between the coughs and the night sweats, I wrote a song called 'Strange Days', trying to make sense of the world as it was changing.

Wren's fever broke, her temperature came down to a normal level, and the coughing stopped. I felt nothing but lucky. We were in lockdown, the pubs were shut, the gigs were off, and it was looking like life might never be the same again, but at least we weren't hooked up to an ICU machine, or worse - a reality that many were facing. I knew I was in no position to complain. Seeing what was happening the world over was as heartbreaking as the stories I heard on my own doorstep. We had a garden, we had each other, and we were alright financially. Thank fuck, I had money in the bank from my last tour. I knew I could pay rent. I could ride this out, as long as it didn't last too long. I spent my days trying to make sure Wren's world stayed as big, as fun and as playful as it was before, even if the playground was shut. We explored Victoria Park and Wick Woodland to keep ourselves occupied, and at night, while she slept, I wrote songs.

I felt the need to record and release the 'Strange Days" song immediately; I don't really know why. But then again, I've never really known why I react to the world around me by writing songs about it. It's just something I've always done. Now it was happening ever faster as the world was speeding up. I also played a livestream gig on my Facebook page. Everyone was doing it. The internet had become a tool for sharing and connecting again, and livestreams were now a thing. The technology was there: all you needed was your phone and you could broadcast yourself to the world live. I was reluctant at first. Why would anyone want to watch me singing songs at home when they could just go to Youtube and watch Bob Dylan singing at Newport Folk Festival in 1965? Or whatever gig their heart desired. It didn't make sense to me, but I found myself tuning into Will Varley and Frank Turner's livestreams, and saw that there was a point: people were using this platform to connect with each other, and everyone was at home looking for something to look at.

Once I got off my high horse, I started to get excited about the livestream. It added a date to a very empty diary. Lizzy and I worked out the best place to put the phone and dressed the living room up as a stage. Making the flyer for the gig almost made me forget everything that was going on in the world. It felt normal for a second. Although odd at first, when it came to show time, I did manage to get into the headspace I would be in if I were playing a real gig. Even if it was just Lizzy sitting, reading out some comments, and giving me a little clap for songs she'd heard a few too many times before. During the performance, I'd given a shout out about my first book, *Drunk Folk Stories.* I had boxes and boxes of them in the shed; the plan was to shift them at gigs and festivals over the summer. I explained this during my performance and, much to my surprise, we sold lots of books - way more than I would at a regular gig. We already had everything we needed to send them out to the world. The system was in place because we'd been doing it ourselves already.

The pandemic went from bad to worse, and it became clear that this wasn't going to end anytime soon. I started spending less time exploring local woodlands with my daughter and writing songs and more time scrolling through my Twitter feed, directly connected to no end of disasters all around the globe. Piled on top of the pandemic was a hellish mix of racism, populism, fascism, nationalism, explosions, food shortages, mental health disasters, conspiracy nutjobs, collapsing economies, the list went on. I'd spent the last few years of my life predicting the breakdown of society and the system as we know it, and here it was unravelling before my eyes. And what was I doing? Fuck all. Just sitting at home reading about it, doing as I was told, writing songs that would affect nothing while filling my head with problems I couldn't fix and driving myself round the bend. All around me, mates that worked in the industry were getting jobs driving for Amazon or signing on for measly benefits. My favourite venues were facing closure, businesses were crumbling, but I felt helpless. I felt a passion for the explosion of the BLM movement. Was it finally time to hold ourselves accountable for our past? If it was, how could I show my support? All the while, people were dying. The death count became a daily fixture, lives being turned into numbers, into data, into charts and graphs that kept on going up. I was writing songs about it but couldn't see how they would help this crazy situation. What could I do? Well, I thought to myself. Give them money. All these causes need money, not a three-chord folk song. I thought about the easiest money I'd ever made: my art. I realised that I had a few boxes of canvases in the shed, underneath the books. Finally, I'd given myself a purpose. I stopped scrolling through my Facebook feed and started putting a plan in place. That night, I wrote up the text that would sit on my website for my first ever online art sale.

As much as the canvases had been a life changing and all-round brilliant move in my life, I'd chosen never to sell them online. For practical reasons, sure, but mainly because I felt it made them more sacred. I still felt like I was taking the piss with them a bit, so I hoped that by keeping them offline I'd keep them interesting. I also liked the idea that not everything was available online. Over the years, plenty of people had emailed me asking for a canvas, but I'd just explained that they'd need to come along to a show.

The world had changed though, so fuck it. My plan was to sell canvases online for one week and give a percentage of the profits to charity. With so many things going wrong, we set it up so that people could pick a charity of their choice. They could choose from the World Health Organisation, the Music Venue Trust or Black Lives Matter. I chose five of my most popular words and slogans for the canvases, and then added an option for a personalised canvas: I'd write whatever people wanted on the canvas for them, just as I would usually after a gig. We announced them on a livestream on Sunday 7th June, and then planned to sell them for one week. We had 500 canvases in the shed, I felt confident we'd sell them all, and on the off chance that we sold more than that, we knew we could get hold of some more easily enough.

It went nuts. We'd sold over 500 canvases before I'd even finished the livestream show. Crazy numbers were coming in. My website crashed at one point, never before having seen traffic anything quite like it. I posted about it the following morning, and the insanity continued. In 24 hours, we'd sold over 1,000 canvases. We ordered some more immediately, we'd made £10,000 overnight, and sales were still coming in thick and fast. I couldn't believe it, I was so fucking chuffed. It meant that Lizzy and I would be all set for a bit, and that I'd contributed towards some of the issues facing the wider world. I felt smug. I know that's not a virtue and nothing to be proud of, but it's the closest I can explain as to how I felt that Monday evening. It was clear I was about to make an extraordinary amount of money from art during one of the most unsettled times in living memory.

Tuesday morning, the telephone rang. It was our landlady. Lizzy pulled an unusual face as she nodded along to a conversation I couldn't hear. Then she started to cry. At least, I could see she was crying, but she was doing it in such a way as to not let Wren know that it was bad news on the line. They were giving us notice. In three months, we would have to leave our home. Amongst all the crazy shit going on, all the uncertainty in the world, now this. Our beautiful home that we treated and loved like our own was about to be taken away, and we had absolutely no say in the matter. It's worth saying here that we had a brilliant relationship with our landlady. She was great. This story is not about bashing landlords, I know there are bad ones out there, but she wasn't one of them. Her son was moving into the house. It had always been the plan, she was giving us plenty of notice, and she was apologetic about the situation, but with lockdown restrictions easing over the summer, she was completely within her legal rights to do so. I didn't blame her, but it still threw up a big pile of confusion for Lizzy and me.

Where would we live? How would we find a home? So many questions, but no time to think about them. The best thing we could do was to get our heads down and make some motherfucking art. I did everything I could to promote the art sale, posting videos and new canvases every day, and asking everyone I knew to share the promo. It worked. The little bad boys just kept on selling, and the money came rolling in.

That week a kind of magic took hold. As I sat down to write the canvases, I started to see the bigger picture, and I felt humbled - which is much better than feeling smug. Two things stood out to me. The canvases' biggest seller said the words 'I'm Home When You Hold Me', the title of the song I'd written back in Chatsworth. I was like Bart Simpson writing lines on the chalkboard board, repeating the same line over and over, I'm home when you hold me, I'm home when you hold me, I'm home when you hold me, the irony being that, as true as that was, we were now in need of a home, and these very words were going to help us. The song had come back to save me. As well as the three charities that we'd been raising money for, there was also an option of the 'Beans family pot' meaning we'd get the full profit from the sale, rather than 50% going to a chosen charity. No, we weren't a charity, but as I explained in the text on the art sale website, I had mouths to feed and rent to pay, and if people wanted the full £10 to come to me, then that was an option. That was overwhelmingly the most popular choice. I sat there writing up my lyrics and personal messages on canvases to people I didn't know, and realised that my songs and my work were coming back to help me in a time when I needed it the most. All of these people would have attended a gig at some point or enjoyed my music, had some kind of connection with what I put out into the world over the years, and now they wanted a piece of art. Maybe it was the handwriting, maybe it was the words, maybe it was the songs, maybe it was people wanting to help out an out-of-work musician, probably a healthy mix of the whole lot, but whatever it was, it connected. The sales continued all week long.

We turned the house into a factory. Friends came around and worked in the garden, packing the canvases and bagging them up. I sat writing all day long, buckets full of maker pens and piles and piles of blank canvases. Outside, crates of packaging filled the drive and piles of ram-packed Royal Mail bags filled the kitchen. Every few hours, the van would be loaded, and we'd take a batch to the Royal Mail delivery office, where Lizzy had charmed the manager into letting us deposit our mail directly into the belly of the beast for it to be shipped out the following day. Lizzy was the factory manager, organising staff, buying more stock, sorting all the paperwork for deliveries and dealing with the many issues that arose. The canvases, it seemed, were going all over the world, from Mexico to Manchester. It kept us busy, and initially, we didn't talk about where we would live or what we planned to do for the next step in our lives. We just got on with it. At the end of the week, we looked up, took a step back, took a deep breath and did the maths:

We'd sold 4,245 pieces of art.

We'd raised over £6,000 for charity.

And after costs and tax, we'd made over £20,000.

Absolute insanity. On top of that, whilst shopping for art many people had picked up a record, a hoodie, a T-shirt or a book. Merch sales hit levels I'd never seen before. We both knew what this meant: with the money we'd made in the last week, combined with the money left from the last tour, we had enough to put down a deposit on a house. Wow.

I never thought I'd leave London. The city that I love. The city where my parents were raised, where I was born. My favourite place in the country - in the world. I've travelled more than most, and as much as I Love New York, Newcastle, Hebden Bridge and São Paulo, never had I been to a place that made me want to leave London and live there instead. I wanted Wren to be a Londoner, to grow up around London's beautiful chaos, with its endless histories and multiculturalism. I wasn't bored of London. I never would be. "This is where I want to live" - that's what I told Lizzy, but that wasn't the point. The point was that we couldn't afford to live there anymore. We'd made this money in an act of pure luck at a time when we needed it the most. Since then, we'd been on the phone with a mortgage advisor, and apparently, now that we had this wedge of a deposit to lay down, we were eligible to borrow money from a bank. The maximum we could borrow was around £300,000. This was obviously fantastic news, life changing. But as crazy as it sounded, three hundred grand in London was bugger all. We couldn't get jack shit in Hackney Wick for that. Not in Leyton or Forest Gate, or even further out.

I was digging my heels in, not annoyed at Lizzy, more with the situation. I wouldn't leave London without a fight, but secretly we both knew where we would go. I'd written it in that song many years before when I said, "the future is an oyster". Whitstable, on the Kent coast. It's where Lizzy is from, where her family are. A scenic fishing town, known for its oysters, its good pubs and stony beaches. "We could move out to the suburbs and have a couple of kids, find somewhere safe to raise them up, preferably by the beach" - another line from the same song. It was fate. Premeditated fate maybe, but fate all the same. I, however, still wasn't letting on.

"Just look at some houses on Rightmove," pleaded Lizzy some more.

I was being annoying and flat out refusing to even consider a move out of London, afraid of change. Unable to imagine what life outside of the city would even look like. She sat out my sulk and waited for me to come around. Once I'd said my piece and stewed on it for a bit, we talked about it again. Lizzy went online and pulled up a house at random, as an example of the sort of thing we could afford in that part of the world. She ran a search in the area and price bracket and then chose a random house that came up. It was the first one I agreed to look at, and it's the house that is now our home. Instantly, it intrigued me. As I started to read about the house, my guard dropped. As well as being way bigger than our Beanacre house, it was one road back from the sea, and it had a vibe. You could tell that even from the pictures. Kind of untraditional in its layout, doing its own thing. It captured my imagination. It also had an out-building at the bottom of the garden, labelled on the floor plan as an art studio. Lizzy explained to me that we could, should we want to, of course, afford to buy this house. We could use the money we'd made in the last week, get the mortgage we'd been told would be approved, and by doing this, we would halve our monthly rent and bills and be paying off our own mortgage, not someone else's. A seed was sown. Maybe I didn't know what life outside the city would look like, but in all fairness, with all that had gone on this year, did I even know what life inside the city would look like? Change was afoot. The reality of a world with fewer gigs and touring was starting to sink in. It was time to adapt. Lockdown had made all of us yearn for the great outdoors. After Wren and I had spent so much time in Wick Woodlands, the idea of the beach, on our doorstep, swimming in the sea whenever we felt like it, sounded lush. I imagined owning a house with an apple tree in the garden. The seed was growing. "Let's go and see it," I said.

We wrapped up the online art sale. It took another week or so of writing, packing and mailing them out, but slowly our house looked less like a factory and more like a house again. It looked different to me now though; it didn't feel like ours anymore, knowing that we had to leave. My interest in the house I'd seen on Rightmove continued to grow. We started to look at other houses in and around the area and the country. None of them interested me in the slightest. There was something about that first house that had clicked. I started to imagine what our lives might look like, living out on the coast. I started to imagine having a studio to work from, to write songs, to write words on blank canvases, and even write another book.

Mortgage advisers, estate agents, solicitors: not really my area of expertise, but we got recommendations from friends and found people we could trust. I had no idea what the process of buying a house looked like. I just knew that everyone always says it's fucking stressful. When we booked in the viewing of the house, my main question was, would we be meeting the person who was selling the house? In the pictures that we'd been staring at relentlessly for the past week, the art studio was filled with beautiful paintings of the sky. I wanted to meet the artist who'd made those pictures.

Her name was Lorraine, and luckily we did get to meet her that day. She was sitting painting a picture of the sky in her studio when the estate agent showed us around. My memory of viewing the place is hard to recall as we've now filled it with our own memories, but I remember that after we'd checked out the main house, we were taken out to the garden to see the studio, where we met Lorraine. Somehow, we started talking about Woodstock, rather than the sale of a house. Lorraine had actually been to Woodstock, on stage too. Straight away, we hit it off. When she found out Lizzy had a professional knowledge of cacti and succulents, she explained that she'd asked the universe just yesterday to send her a plant expert. It seemed she'd been having trouble repotting a money tree. At one point, I was about to smash open the pot restricting the thing from growing. The poor estate agent just stood quietly in the corner, not knowing how to react while the three of us chatted like old friends. She'd built the studio for her painting. Half the roof of the large wooden structure was an open skylight, and the afternoon sun shone through beautifully. It was private, quiet, and it stole my heart. We'd also been asking the universe for some favours of late, and after seeing the house, I knew we had some more asking to do. This was where I wanted to live.

It turns out that everyone was right. Maybe not about everything, but about the whole 'moving house being stressful' thing. Yep, they are right about that. The next few months were long, unsettled and scary. Our mortgage was turned down, banks were understaffed, lawyers were off sick, every question took a week to get answered. Things dragged on, but we managed to secure another mortgage. We managed to keep the house purely from our communication with Lorraine. Talking to her made sense to me. Talking to a bank did not. We spoke regularly, as humans, while the contracts were to-ing and fro-ing. The friendship that we'd struck during that brief meeting gave everyone the patience that was needed to hold out until the mortgage was approved, which, finally, it was. The plan was to move out at the end of October, one month before my 40th birthday. The relief was insane; my head had been doing an erratic dance for the past couple of months, and we didn't have a backup plan. We put all our hearts and plans into this one house.

I had been visualising it, willing it to happen, more than I had anything else in my whole life. As the decision was out of my hands, all I could do was try to manifest a future that I wanted, for me, Lizzy and Wren. I can specifically remember placing myself at a desk in the art studio. I promised myself that, if everything went to plan, then I'd write a new book, and the final chapter would be the story of how I came to buy a house and how I came to be sat at my own desk in my own studio writing it. And, ladies and gentlemen, here we are.

The story of a 40-year-old man managing to buy a house in the country he was born in might not be deemed a success story for many, but there you go. I can only talk about my experience of events, and from where I'm standing, I like the view. I didn't even tell Lizzy's story, setting up her own company selling plants and cacti, which also made all of this possible, or the other story, which is the story between Wren and I. That's a fairy tale that has run alongside this one, one that I couldn't even begin to describe using words on a page or paint on a canvas. Nothing would ever do it justice.

We've been in the house now for four months, and we love our new home. So far, that time has all been in lockdown, but we've been busy - busy making our house our home, busy making Wren's world bigger as she grows and learns and dazzles us, busy getting to know the neighbours and the area, busy watching the tide come and go, busy writing music and busy writing this book.

The studio is everything I hoped it would be. A place to be creative, not just for me, but for all of us. Wren loves it out here, splashing her paint all over the shop, and Lizzy has as many cacti, flowers and plants coming and going as I do songs. We moved just before my latest album was released, and the studio turned into a factory for the release. The Royal Mail delivery bags were back, but this time around, they weren't piled high in the kitchen. For what we do and what we need, it's perfect.

Things going down like this have given me a newfound sense of purpose. I'm not sure if I've got this house through luck, talent, timing, or fate, but I feel like it was a gift from all of the people who have listened to my music, and now I feel like I owe it to them to honour it. I owe it to them to take this opportunity, this comfort and this creative space and to put my heart on the line, to sing songs about why I think the world is a beautiful and special place, to do what I can to inspire others to be good, to be optimistic and to find their path, love and happiness. Regardless of the backdrop, these are our lives that we're leading. Let's enjoy them and put a little bit of good into the world as we go. Let us believe in ourselves, in our future and in each other, let us believe in love and, last of all: let us believe in art.

OUTRO

Booom! There you have it. Thanks again for reading my book, I've just sat down and gone through it for the last time before it goes off to print. I started this book back in March 2020, as lockdown in the UK began, and today, 12th April 2021, is a seminal day for us here as pubs, shops and life start to reopen again and we will once again be able to see our friends and family. I'm still in no place to comment on what the future holds but as it stands gigs and festivals are on the horizon, and I'll remain hopeful and positive that they will go ahead. If not, we'll adapt and survive.

It's been a lot of fun digging through old memories and re-living these stories in my head in order to get them onto the page. Life has been good to me. I'm not normally one to get nostalgic but I was lucky to be part of it. Whatever the future does hold, I'm up for it and I'm confident there will be more songs, more blags, more art and in turn, more stories. Long may it continue.

ISBN 978-1-9168824-0-9

Printed and bound by Clays Ltd in the UK

www.beansontoastmusic.com